Everyday colour

Alison Standish

First published in 2015

ISBN 978-0-9558669-6-8

Cover and mandalas designed by Garry Robson – www.garryrobson.co.uk
Designed and typeset by Helius
www.helius.biz

Printed in the UK

Contents

Introduction

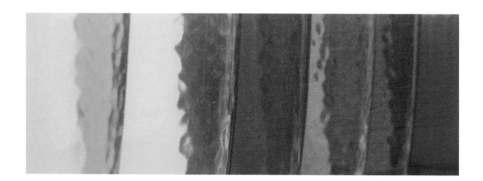

Colour is everywhere, there is no getting away from it – we see it, we eat it, we wear it and we even breathe it. How boring our life would be without colour, just a journey of 'black and white'.

I am Alison Standish, the Colour Minister and founder of The Colour Ministry. I have written this book as a result of 20 years' experience and study as a Colour Therapist, and have incorporated valuable information from other 'colour gurus'.

Explore the amazing world of colour, by delving into some basic history and science, and trying out hints and tips on how you can benefit by adding colour to your life.

Everyday Colour is designed as a 'dip in and dip out' read, and contains plenty of information, including:

- why and how colour affects us, both physically and emotionally
- how you can improve your health and wellbeing using colour
- what the colours that you wear say about you and what you are telling the people around you
- how to create uplifting, stress-free homes and workspaces
- how developing a physiological understanding of colour can help you brand your business and project your personal identity.

Introduction

I use the nine-colour system, which has been used as a basis of colour therapy for many years. However, I have adapted these techniques to incorporate some 21st century ideas that make 'colour and light' a leading tool for everyday use, creating a healthier and more positive *you*.

Colour and colour therapy

For us to exist we need light. Since the beginning of time, whether considering the 'big bang' theory or the creation of the Earth as described in sacred texts, light is the first requirement of life.

Colour is light broken down into frequencies, and it is these frequencies that we use to help us distinguish certain colours (see the sections on basic science and colour biology later in this book for more in-depth information).

Colour has been used for over 3 million years. Stone-age cave paintings verify that people used colour to describe scenes of the time, and in the past food would have been identified as edible by its unique colours (i.e. berries and plants). Numerous artefacts and manuscripts from ancient times show the importance of colour and its impact at different times throughout history.

Colour and colour therapy

In this book you will discover the world of colour from a 'colour therapy' standpoint. Colour therapy takes the frequencies of the different colours to help create harmony and balance of the mind, body and spirit. These techniques can then be put together to create a broader understanding of how colour works in our 'everyday' world and how we can harness these special energies to help us live a more positive and joyful life.

History of colour therapy

Colour therapy and the use of colour in healing treatments has been around for a very long time. Documents written on papyrus by the Egyptians, and dating back as far as 2000 BC, contain information on the use of colour rooms to help heal various diseases. Egyptians considered the body and the mind together when diagnosing illness (the conscious and the unconscious). Not only did they use the practical essences of colour, they also wore amulets and created prayers to various gods, which they would repeat (sound is also a vibration) to help change mindset and create a new consciousness.

In many ancient civilisations, priests were also medical practitioners, as evidenced by documentation dating back to before 2000 BC. The *Vendidad*, an ecclesiastical text from Iran (Persia), talks of illness and the natural cures of colour to support life.

It is understood that many myths and stories are closely associated with the Indian 'Vedas' – Hindu documents dating back to before 4000 BC. The Vedas, which contain the Eight Tenets, include a hefty contribution regarding colour healing, and man is seen in the Hindu tradition as the visible colours of the spectrum.

There is further discussion in ancient texts on how meditation allows us to reach our own internal powers – through the use of breath it enables us to bring the healing from 'within' to 'without'. The Ayurvedic traditions follow these principles, incorporating diet, colour, meditation and balance in their healing philosophies.

As well as the Hindus over 3000 years ago, China has also contributed a great deal to colour healing. Chinese medicine uses the Five Colours, Five Elements, Five Tastes, Four Situations and Four Seasons. The five colours are green, red, white, yellow and black. These are incorporated in healing recipes, which also include the use of meridians in the body. The meridian lines are described as 'energy flow', and the Chinese devised techniques that a physician could use to increase or decrease the flow and heal the body.

In Chinese medicine the use of yin energy, which is masculine and positive, and yang energy, which is feminine and negative, allows the body and the mind to become balanced. The energy is seen to work from the inside of the body to the outside. This differs from the Western cultural view, which sees 'stress' as coming from the outside and eventually becoming 'within'. In Western cultures colour therapy is considered a complementary therapy not a 'mainstream' solution.

When we go to the doctor in our Western culture we are being treated for the symptoms of our illnesses but are not necessarily being treated with a view to obtaining an overall cure. However, it is quite apparent, especially in complementary medicine, that to be 'well' we must treat the mind and body connection as one organism.

When using colour therapy in the UK, we generally apply techniques of correcting overexposure, either physical or mental, by balancing the body with complementary colours. For example, for too much overthinking and analysing (yellow) purple is used to rebalance.

Our brain is composed of two parts, the left-hand and the right-hand sides. The left-hand side of the brain activates the right-hand side of the body, and vice versa. The left brain deals with analytical thought, logic, the written word, numbers and reasoning, while the right brain deals with creativity, music, imagination, intuition, art and holistic thought. For us to be in balance we have to use both parts of the brain simultaneously.

The two parts of the brain are related to different functions of our bodies, and we create various hormones both from a physico-chemical reactions and also from our emotional reactions. Using light and specific colours can help balance these hormones, which in turn helps our bodies heal and creates positive wellbeing. Whether absorbed by our eyes, absorbed through our skin or ingested in our diet, colour eventually finds its way to all locations within the body.

Light and colour – the basic science

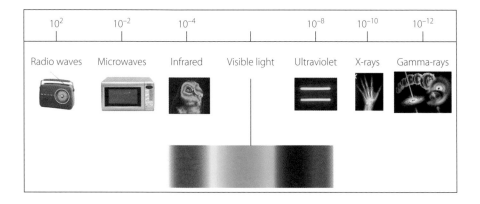

Light is made up of energy waves or particles, which are grouped together according to their energy. A light wave consists of energy in the form of electromagnetic (electric and magnetic) fields. There are many electromagnetic fields, ranging from sound waves (lowest frequency) through to gamma rays (highest frequency). The frequencies of these waves are measured in nanometres (nm, one thousand millionth of a metre) or hertz (Hz, cycles per second). Nanometres measure the interval between the peaks of the waves (wavelength), and hertz measures the refresh rate per cycle (frequency).

The visible spectrum (*spectrum* is the Latin word for 'appearance' or 'apparition') is one group of these fields. Each of the visible colours has a different interval and speed, although all light travels at approximately 186,000 miles per second. Each colour has its own wavelength, starting with red at approximately 700 nm and ending with violet at approximately 400 nm. In layman's terms, the visible spectrum starts with the colour red, which has the longest wavelength and the lowest frequency, and then as the wavelengths get shorter and the frequencies get higher the colours move through the spectrum.

The spectrum starts with the colour red, which emanates from the heat elements of microwave and infrared. Travelling through the visible spectrum, the colours lead to violet, which has a short wavelength and high frequency and thus creates a cooler energy.

Colour scientists

The first Western colour scientist/guru was **Hippocrates**, who studied colour over two millennia ago (*c*. 460–377 BC). He used red for fire, yellow for air, blue for water and green for earth.

In the 13th century, **Roger Bacon** theorised that rainbows were produced when light shone through glass or a crystal. It was not until the 1600s, when **Isaac Newton** (interestingly he was born on 25th December) developed the principles of colour. Taking a prism and placing it in front of a ray of light, Newton noticed that the light refracted (split) into seven different coloured rays: red, orange, yellow, green, blue, indigo and violet.

Artists were fascinated by his discovery and especially by the fact that Newton created a circle with the colours opposing each other, i.e. the 'colour wheel' we are familiar with today.

In the 1800s, **Goethe**, a German scientist, discovered the mechanics of human vision. He deciphered that our brain processes information received from the mechanics of our eyes – what we see of an object depends on the object, the lighting and our own perception. Goethe also talked about human emotions in terms of colour, and explained that the 'plus' colours (the yellows and oranges) were positive, uplifting and warm, and the 'minus' colours (the blues) were cool, melancholy and weaker. These observations are still relevant today, as you will see once you start working with the individual colours.

Steiner, a German philosopher working in the late 1800s and very much a follower of Goethe and his theories, applied a highly spiritual approach to colour, showing that a human being's life is a journey of colour and that colour plays an important role both emotionally as well as physically. Today there are 40 Steiner schools in the UK. These offer schooling from a different perspective, and incorporate colour in everyday learning and development.

D. P. Ghadiali, a Hindu scientist also working in the late 1800s, formulated the scientific principles behind the different effects that different colours have on the human body. Ghadiali found that for each organism or system there was a particular colour that stimulated and another that inhibited its functioning. Concluding that balance could be restored by treatment with the appropriate colour he developed a system of healing using coloured lights, which he called the *Spectro-Chrome*.

Also in the late 1800s, **Edward Babbitt** published a book called *The Principles of Light and Colour*, in which he described the healing effects and attributes of each of the seven colours. This work is the basis of modern colour therapy.

Babbitt also invented devices such as the *Chromalume*, which involved exposure to sunlight through coloured glass. This method is used today in the treatment of seasonal affective disorder (SAD) using coloured lamps.

In the 1920s, **Ivah Bergh Whitten** created the Amica Master Institute of Color Awareness and wrote some of the first books on colour therapy from a holistic perspective.

In the 1930s, **Faber Birren** became an Industrial Colour Consultant, advising on the psychological effects of colour with regard to safety, employee morale, productivity and sales. He wrote 40 books and over 200 articles on the subject.

In the 1960s, **Max Lüscher** created his colour psychology test, which deals with personality types as identified from their colours.

Theo Gimbel's colour spine chart, which he produced in the 1980s, deals with issues related to the physical, emotional, mental or spiritual energy sources of the body.

Today there is extensive knowledge about colour therapy and its healing qualities, but for most people the medical treatment of choice is still pharmaceutical drugs.

Colour biology

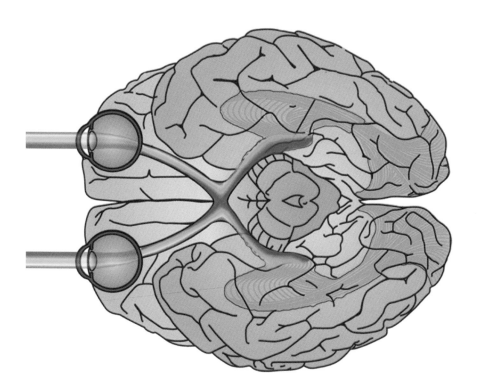

Why do we need light and colour?

Light helps the body regulate our melatonin levels which let us know when to wake and when to sleep. Light also helps us to rebuild our immune systems so that we can fight off disease and illness.

When light refracts as it hits objects it displays various colours, and these colours make up the full spectrum of light. Not only does light help us to see and identify objects but it can also travel through our bodily systems and affect certain functions of our organs and stimulate certain information in our brains.

In his book *Light, Medicine of the Future*, Dr Jacob Lieberman, a world-renowned optometrist, states that only 25% of light that is absorbed through the eyes is used for vision, while the other 75% travels through the optic pathways to the brain. Therefore colours route to exact locations of the body, and if there are imbalances colours can rebalance those organs.

How we see colour

Light shines on the retina and is converted to impulses that are sent to the brain. **Rods** (120 million) and **cones** (6 to 7 million) in the eye contain a pigment that, when the light is absorbed, breaks down into substances which are sent to the brain and pineal gland and around the body.

The rods in our retina enable us to distinguish between light and no light, but the action of cones is a little more complicated. We have three sets of cones (red, green and blue), so we are only capable of truly seeing these colours. However, our brain mixes the red, green and blue signals and transforms them into colours. The various lengths of signals our brain receives in these three colours allows it to mix a palette, making millions of colours from just three. We are unable to see colours in the dark, as our rods are only capable of showing us light or no light.

Colour and light are also absorbed directly by the skin. When we disrupt these patterns of exposure or use artificial light our bodies become confused and our hormones become unbalanced, and this can lead to health-related issues. For example, we require exposure to sunlight for our bodies to synthesis vitamin D, which is essential for everyday health and vitality. Colour therapy assists with regulating and balancing our systems through the use of complementary colours.

Our auric energy fields

Each of us is made up of predominantly (99%) carbon, oxygen, water, hydrogen and nitrogen, all of which are chemicals. In daily life our bodies respond to signals sent from our brain and around our nervous system, and we then react.

We are constantly moving and vibrating with millions of these signals, every second our bodies are electric. The field around our body, the auric field, is a two-way filter between the outside world and our physical bodies.

Exercise to feel your 'auric field'

1. Rub your hands together fairly quickly and you will start to feel heat build-up.
2. Pull your hands away about 3 inches and see if you can still feel the heat or a tingling in the palms.
3. Move your hands gently further apart and notice when the heat or tingling stops.
4. You can also do this by standing close to someone and both of you rubbing your hands.
5. Place your hands in front of you and then move towards the other person. Can you feel tingling or heat from them? If so, you are now feeling their aura.

Our aura cannot only be felt it can be seen (as per the picture on page 17 that was taken with an aura camera).

As colour is a frequency, then so are you, and the combination gives an array of colours that interprets how you are feeling and what you are experiencing in a particular moment. In our day-to-day existence we collect positive and negative frequencies within our energy fields. Without clearing our energy fields (the aura) we can turn *dis-ease* into disease, which filters into our physical bodies.

The aura and energy points (the 'chakras') in our body

The earliest information regarding chakras dates back to 1700 BC and they are mentioned in the Vedas, the early Hindu books, where they are described as breathing channels. Chakras also appear in Buddhist traditions and Eastern philosophies, and have been part of the ancient art of energy healing for many years.

'Chakra' is the Sanskrit word for 'wheel'. Chakras are explained, in complementary, Chinese and Ayurvedic healing as the places in our body where energy is transferred from our 'aura' into our physical bodies, and vice versa. Transfer of energy then takes place by making contact with our spinal fluid and travelling around our system. If we have been collecting negative energies then these can unbalance our chakras and make them spin either very quickly, very slowly or break down altogether.

Each chakra is recognised as a certain colour. In colour therapy there are two additional chakras, one just outside the body above our head in the auric field and another located higher towards the ether.

The chakras and their positions in the body

Base of the body – Base chakra – Red

Below the stomach – Sacral chakra – Orange

At the stomach – Solar plexus chakra – Yellow

At the heart – Heart chakra – Green

At the throat – Throat chakra – blue

At the eyebrows – Brow/third-eye chakra – Indigo

At the crown – Crown chakra – Purple

Above the head – Soul star – Magenta

Higher than the soul star – Stellar chakra – Gold

Rebalancing and cleansing the chakras is one of the key areas of colour therapy, and most people who come for a treatment will automatically get their chakras balanced.

Colour therapists also use other key areas known as 'meridian points', which are located throughout the body and act like an energy bloodstream, keeping the flow of energy around our physical bodies balanced. Colours can also be used on these points to help stimulate and direct the flow, clearing blockages and balancing disruption.

Colour therapy is a complementary healing process, so if you are concerned about any aspects of your health then do go and see your doctor.

Colour personalities

Getting to know your colour personality is a very useful tool in understanding yourself and others from a colour perspective. By using an ancient technique that incorporates numerology and colour together you can calculate your personality colour.

I use this technique on a daily basis in my work, and over the last 20 years I have been amazed by how accurately a person's traits are reflected by their colour personality.

Colour personalities

In many of my colour healing sessions I use the technique to calculate the colours of individuals and applying those colours in treatments that will increase the personality colour for vitality and energy. Alternatively, I use complementary colours that will react and balance the personality colour when it is over-energised, creating calm and tranquillity.

Learning your colour personality is also fun and gives a valuable insight into partnership dynamics, family dynamics and even the dynamics operating in a team-working environment. It brings together in a very individual way our understanding of how colour affects us personally and how the colour in the environment reacts with our vibrational frequency.

You can learn more about your colour personality from our book *Know Your Colour Personality* (available from our website colourministry.co.uk, or Amazon.co.uk). The book contains sections on each colour, and provides further information on your personality colour and how you can balance your personality traits.

Colour for printing

The CMYK colour model (process colour, four colour) is a subtractive colour model used in colour printing, and the term is also used to describe the printing process itself.

CMYK refers to the four inks used in some colour printing: cyan, magenta, yellow, and key (black). Although it varies by print house, press operator, press manufacturer, and press run, ink is typically applied in the order of the abbreviation.

The K in CMYK stands for 'key' because in four-colour printing, cyan, magenta and yellow printing plates are carefully keyed, or aligned, with the key of the black key plate. Some sources suggest that the K in CMYK comes from the last letter in 'black' and was chosen because B already means blue. However, this explanation, although useful as a mnemonic, is incorrect. K is used to denote 'key', which was possibly chosen because black is often used as an outline.

The CMYK model works by partially or entirely masking colours on a lighter, usually white, background. The ink reduces the light that would otherwise be reflected. Such a model is called 'subtractive', because inks 'subtract' brightness from white.

In the CMYK model white is the natural colour of the paper or other background, black results from a full combination of coloured inks. To save money on ink, and to produce deeper black tones, using black ink instead of the combination of cyan, magenta and yellow produces unsaturated and dark colours.

A study done by a major publication revealed that the use of colour increased readership by 40% or more, and a university study showed a 65% increase in the retention of material when full colour was used instead of black and white.

Colour in technology

When we watch TV or look at a tablet, mobile phone or computer screen we see a wide range of colours, or we think we do. These devices use the RGB colour model. This is an 'additive' colour model, in which red, green and blue light are added together in various ways to reproduce a broad array of colours. The name of the model comes from the initials of the three additive primary colours: red, green and blue.

The main use of the RGB colour model is in the sensing, representation and display of images in electronic systems, such as TVs and computers, although it has also been used in conventional photography.

Colour in technology

Each pixel on the screen is built by driving three small and very close, but still separate, RGB light sources. At a common viewing distance the separate sources are indistinguishable, which tricks the eye into seeing a particular solid colour. All the pixels arranged together on the rectangular screen make the colour image. You are therefore in reality seeing a combination of red green and blue for every colour.

Individual colours

You have now seen how complex colour can be. The following sections deal with the colours individually, and each section covers:

- the history of the colour
- how the colour affects us physically and emotionally
- the healing properties of the colour
- wearing the colour
- using the colour in your environment
- using the colour in business
- the basic colour personalities.

In line with its complexity colour is very subjective, so do feel free to disagree with my findings.

Red

Red is probably the most talked about colour of the visible spectrum and the colour that causes the most controversy.

It is an important sign of dominance for primates – when their skin turns red, you know who is in charge, and maybe that is where 'seeing red' comes from. Blushing females give off positive signals to attract mates.

History of red

In the natural world red appears in fruits, berries and flowers, and it may have been one of the first colours that man recognised with the naked eye. For humans, blushing can attract mates, and definitely gives us the signal that someone is reacting to our energies.

Red was used over 170,000 years ago when stone-age humans used ochre to colour their bodies and paint images of bison on the walls of their caves, reminding them of life and death.

Madder was the first plant dye used widely in Europe, Asia and Africa, and the first artists who mixed paint used white, black and red as their primary art colours. In Ancient Egyptian and Mayan cultures, revellers would paint themselves red with madder and wear red robes. The women would wear red cosmetics on their cheeks and lips to enhance their beauty and attract male admirers.

Roman soldiers wore red cloaks to depict courage and strength, and many a gladiator was painted with red ochre prior to a fight.

In South America a stronger red, produced using a dye obtained from an insect (either the *Kermes* or the cochineal), was used. Various shades were created when the red dye was mixed with different pigments.

In China, they also dyed robes red using the madder plant, and red soon became the colour of emperors and senior officials, displaying their wealth and authority.

In the Middle Ages, the Catholic Church adopted red as the colour of majesty and authority. The colour represented the blood of Christ and played an important role in many rituals. Cardinals, bishops and senior church officials wore red robes.

Later, brighter reds from South America began to appear but, as the cochineal was fairly rare and expensive, only those with great incomes could afford the colour. These individuals included bankers and courtesans – which is maybe where the 'red light' district got its name.

By the 18th and 19th centuries the colour red had become a symbol of liberty and personal freedom. France adopted the colour for its flag, and socialism was born.

Meanwhile, in China, red had always played an important role in the national culture – their flag is red, and their emperors and senior soldiers and fighters wore red. Red is associated with the element of fire, one of the six important elements that form the basis of the Chinese philosophy of life.

In the 20th and 21st centuries red became the colour of revolution, in particular it is the colour of the communist party. The impressionist artist Henri Matisse chose to paint with a more bluish red to portray feelings within his canvases. These were the first days of painting emotions, with red showing an array of emotions from anger to joy. Later, in the 1960s, Mark Rothko used blocks of red on large canvasses to inspire deep emotions.

Today red is used for every emergency sign around the globe, expressing caution. Indian and Chinese brides wear red on their wedding day to represent luck and happiness.

Physical and emotional aspects of red

Red is an active colour, increasing our blood pressure, raising the heart rate and speeding up the circulation. Our adrenaline is activated by the frequency of red, giving rise to our adrenaline-fuelled flight or fight responses.

Red is the warmest of all the colours and is related to fire. Its warmth gives rise to heat so our natural reaction to red is to feel physically a few degrees warmer.

Red is related to the base chakra of the body and activates our ability of self-awareness (see the chakra chart on page 20) It deals with our feet, legs, hips and genitalia. It connects us directly to the Earth and makes us feel grounded, safe and secure.

Red stimulates passion and desire; it gives us courage to face situations that we may be unable to face. Red is related to our sexual desires, survival and basic instincts.

For some people red can feel aggressive and harsh, overwhelming and angry. As a colour it can be challenging and very direct.

Leadership and independence are traits of red. Red ties are worn by political leaders when they wish to take on challenging issues and have a direct 'stab' at other parties and members of the media.

Red as a healing colour

Red helps to balance and heal the following conditions:

- Anaemia – increases iron in the blood.
- Low blood pressure – increases blood circulation and heart rhythm.
- Colds – dries mucous and adds warmth.
- Menstruation problems – eases blood circulation.
- Pneumonia – provides warmth and dries mucous.
- Low libido –increases sex drive.
- Kidney problems – stimulates kidney function.
- Skin conditions, sores – purifies the skin.

Our levels of vitamin B are increased when we use the colour red.

We need, however, to be cautious when applying red as a healing colour. It can overstimulate our organs and can create adverse reactions of anger and agitation. I have used the following techniques to add the colour red when healing.

Red solarised water

I have found that using water solarised with red is one of the best ways to ingest this colour. This technique has the same impact physically as using a red light but has a subtler effect on the emotions.

The quickest way to prepare solarised water is to purchase a red glass from a local stockist and fill it with fresh filtered water. Put the glass in a light location for about 20 minutes and let the colour infuse into the water vibrationally. Then drink the water.

Alternatively, you can make your own solarised water by filling a glass bottle or jug with filtered water and wrapping it in the colour red (e.g. a scarf or coloured paper). Place the wrapped vessel in a light location for 20 minutes, and then drink the water.

Red scarf or red fabric

Remove any clothing or wear something white over your legs and take 15 minutes out of your day to sit with either a red scarf or piece of red fabric wrapped around your hips or over your legs. The better the quality of the fabric the better the experience, so silk and cashmere are great for their vibrational qualities. Tuck yourself in, close your eyes and focus on the red fabric.

Allow the red vibration to seep through your skin, and be aware that this colour is working with the base of your body. This colour will activate the base chakra, and red will pour into your aura and work its way into your physical system.

The technique is gentle and subliminal. Apply it for 15 minutes every day until you feel yourself responding to the colour by having more energy and more vitality.

When not to use red in healing

Red should not be used if you are feeling overstimulated by life. Anxiety, chronic fatigue, myalgic encephalopathy (ME), attention deficit hyperactivity disorder (ADHD), epilepsy and other disorders are affected by the overuse of red, so do be careful when using this colour.

I personally tend to use orange as an alternative to red in treatments when I am unsure of how a client will react.

What happens when you wear red

When you wear red you are making a statement. It is a colour that projects leadership and confidence. There are many variations of red but here we are talking about a striking red. I tend to use this colour as an accent colour only, and in the winter a red scarf, hat and gloves keep me lovely and warm.

It is still a power colour, and when worn in the correct shade can look extremely sexy. Research reveals that men love women in red as it enhances their sex appeal and they appear more approachable. It also denotes that this particular woman is not adverse to a sexual relationship and is open about the intention by wearing the colour. The dating site OkCupid claims that women who are wearing red in their personal profile picture get more messages and dates than those who wear another colour. Wearing red for men is not quite so attractive according to some reports, as it can be mistaken for dominance and control.

Another body of research states that when women are ovulating they tend to wear red to attract a mate. If you are trying to get pregnant, then wear red.

Other research from Durham University in the UK has shown that on men red can appear as dominant and aggressive and can seem to be an unfair advantage in competitive sport. I tend to look at politicians' ties to see what colours they use to communicate their point of view, with red being about change and moving forward.

When you are wearing red remember that other people are feeling this vibration as well as you. So if you want confidence and to 'strut your stuff' but don't want it all on show, then wear red underwear and smile.

Adding red into your environment

As we can see red is a stimulant, so use it sparingly in the bedroom as it could keep you awake, unless of course that is what you require.

Red is very striking as an accent wall colour in a room but can be overwhelming if applied to all the walls.

I use red in my office when I need to be 'doing' instead of creating or analysing. Usually I will incorporate a painting or a mandala (a picture designed for healing) that I have coloured or painted to help bring in the vibration of red.

Alternatively, you can also use coloured bottles or glasses on window ledges so that when the item captures sunlight it fills the entire space with the red vibration. You can also use crystals and stones; red jasper will give the vibrational frequency of red, creating stimulation and movement.

Red for business

There are many organisations that use bed in their logo and branding: Vodafone, Virgin, MacDonald's, Pizza Hut, Burger King Pirelli, Ferrari, Mitsubishi, Citroën, Firestone, Puma, Coca Cola, Red Bull plus many more.

Red implies movement and speed. Companies involved in mobile phone and broadband, travel, fast food, sports gear, energy drinks and fast cars are all giving a subliminal message of these traits.

If your business or service fits into this category then red may be the colour that you would like to include in your logo or branding. Do be careful though, as red is a dominant and strong colour and some people can be easily 'put off' by its power.

It has to be well thought through. Take, for example, Nike's logo in red with the strapline that says 'Just do it'. This works as the red gives further emphasis to the invitation in the strapline.

Many organisations use red as an accent colour so as not to overpower their customers. This works exceptionally well for companies such as Red Hat, Red Lion and Adobe where the whole logo is not red.

However, note that all signs which indicate a need to take action (e.g. 'Sale', 'Discounted' or 'Reductions') are red, so if you need to grab attention then red is the colour to help you do so.

Red personalities

Red relates to the number 1 and people with a red personality have the following traits:

Vibrant, busy, lively ● Quick tempered ● Direct ● Passionate, driven, competitive ● Doesn't hold grudges ● Focused on oneself ● Impatient, never still

Red celebrities: Eric Morecambe, Prince Phillip, James Martin.

Balance colours for red

As red is an energetic colour then the balance colours are green and blue, which enhance relaxation, harmony and coolness, leading to a general slowing of energy.

Nature is good for red personalities, allowing them to take a bigger breath and slow down. The use of blue and green around the house is also ideal.

For red kids their energy will be highly active, and they tend to 'crash and burn' before rebuilding. I would make sure that their bedrooms were either green or blue, giving them space to relax and rebuild. As they have a great deal of energy, anything that expends energy will help support them through life.

Orange

Orange is not a very popular colour for clothing among women in the northern hemisphere, as it tends to clash with paler skin colours when worn, while darker skinned women find it more appealing. Men, on the other hand, tend not to take such a strong dislike to the colour.

History of orange

The colour orange is named after the orange fruit, coming from the Spanish word *naranja* meaning 'orange'.

The Ancient Egyptians used an orange or red-yellow pigment called 'realgar' in their tomb paintings, among many other things. The Romans traded in the mineral 'orpiment', which was used in China as a medicine, although it is highly toxic.

In the 18th and 19th centuries, the Orange royal household was very influential in Europe. William I of Orange organised the Dutch resistance against Spain and fought for the Netherlands to gain its independence, after which orange became the colour of the Dutch. William II became King of England and the Netherlands. He was a protestant and introduced the colour into the UK's political movement, hence 'Orangemen'.

In art, orange was a fairly prominent colour in the paintings of the Pre-Raphaelites in the 19th century, and was even more evident in the paintings by the Impressionists in the later part of the 19th century, who often used orange as a background colour and for clothing.

Saffron, from the flowers of the *Crocus sativus* plant, is used both as a dye and a spice. Turmeric, from the rhizomes of the *Curcuma longa* plant, is a less expensive substitute for saffron.

Alternative dyes and pigments derived from lead oxide were manufactured from around the time of the Ancient Egyptians, but most of these pigments were toxic. They were replaced at the beginning of the 20th century by cadmium orange and chrome orange, which are synthetic and much safer compounds. These products are now used in a great deal of our foods as E100 numbered additives.

Orange is the colour of autumn, mainly because many plants and fruits contain carotenes, pigments that turn fruit and vegetables orange at this time of year. The pigments convert the light energy absorbed from the sun into energy to help the plant's growth. The name 'carrot' comes from the word 'carotene'.

Physical and emotional aspects of orange

Whether you like or dislike orange, it is a colour that tends to make people smile. The beneficial healing power of orange increases our 'feel-good' feelings by increasing our serotonin levels.

Orange also physically stimulates us, but in a more restraint manner than red. Its stimulation is great for creativity and for 'birthing' projects and ideas.

Sensuality and sexuality are increased by orange as it works with the sacral chakra of the body and brings about the traits and understanding of self-respect. The sacral chakra is linked to dance and music. Dance was originally created for women to attract men by displaying their hip-to-waist ratio, which indicated to admiring men whether a woman was capable of carrying their seed.

Orange is the colour of freedom, and a number of flags contain the colour (e.g. Ireland, India, Ghana and Niger). It is also an antidote to grief, as it allows the 'letting go' of people, places and any of life's dramas.

An emotional colour, orange is also linked to food, so you may find yourself eating more if you are in an orange kitchen or dining area. So do be a little careful when using this colour in food areas, as it can create overeating and expansive waistlines.

Orange creates an energy that increases social interaction, joyfulness, humour and generosity among groups of people, bringing an easy and relaxed flow to celebrations and festivities.

It can also be a risk-taking colour, so if you add it to your environment then you will stimulate the energy to help you change or move forward.

Orange as a healing colour

Orange increases the vitamin C in our bodies and helps to balance and heal the following conditions:

- Cramps – anywhere in the body as it frees the flow.
- Respiratory system – stimulates and frees breathing.
- Thyroid – stimulates an underactive thyroid.
- Depression – a great anti-depressant.
- Reproduction – stimulates the reproductive system.
- Dispels fear – decreases anxiety and stress.
- Shock/trauma – stabilises the physical body after a shock.

I use orange with clients who are suffering with depression or feeling very 'blue', as it is the complementary colour to blue and is naturally uplifting.

It is also a great colour for soothing the digestive system and is anti-inflammatory.

Orange glasses

Wearing glasses with orange lenses helps support the gradual ease from depression by enhancing the letting go of anxiety and fear and assisting in moving towards joy and happiness. I use PRiSMA glasses with my clients, but you can purchase any type of orange glasses (available from our website: colourministry.co.uk).

Wear the glasses for 10 minutes in the morning and 10 minutes in the early afternoon for as long as you feel necessary. These timings can be increased during the winter, as we get less light and our vitamin D levels fall. I increase the time to about 20 minutes for each session. These glasses will help support an increase in your serotonin levels and make you feel as though you are on holiday!

There is evidence that using orange-coloured glasses at night when using a tablet, phone or other electronic device may help you sleep as the glasses reduce the amount of blue light that is being fed through to your brain from the rods and cones in your eyes. Good-quality sleep is a must for your body to be healthy, and can definitely reduce the feeling of being depressed.

Orange foods

If you really don't like the colour orange in a visual sense then increasing your intake of orange foods will help you to add orange into your daily life.

Orange foods include egg yolks, smoked fish, lentils, grains, carrots, swede, sweet potato, pumpkin, pumpkin seeds, tahini, paw, mangos, citrus fruits, spices and many more.

Adding turmeric (the orange colour in curry) to your favourite winter casserole increases your intake of the colour. It is an anti-oxidant and anti-inflammatory spice, so it calms your digestive system and relieves any types of cramps. It also improves your serotonin levels and is fantastic for arthritis too.

Using ginger in a tea will aid digestion and clear sinuses, so is fantastic to use in the winter.

Sweet potatoes are a great substitute for normal potatoes as the additional nutrients they contain help boost the immune system and prevent heart disease. They are also fantastic for balancing out your sugar levels, which is great for diabetics.

When not to use orange in healing

I have always applied orange in all of my treatments, as we are not overstimulated by this colour in the UK. However, sometimes orange can expose blockages on a physical and emotional level, so do be aware that emotions can run high when you add the colour to your life.

What happens when you wear orange

Over the past few years we have seen a revival of the colour orange in clothing. The tone of orange is very relevant here, and I have found that I have to try the different tones and shades to see how it reacts with my skin colour.

In a recent business poll, 25% of employers stated that they felt a candidate wearing orange was unprofessional. I think this relates back to the 'play' element of the colour. I would, therefore, suggest that orange is used as an accent colour by wearing it in a scarf or a top. I would combine it with a rich brown or suede in the winter and white and aqua in the summer to give off a cheery energy.

I wear orange when I am out and about with friends and having fun. I find it an optimistic colour and it definitely brings a smile to people's faces. I can always be spotted too!

Monks and spiritual individuals wear a great deal of orange, or saffron. It is a spiritual colour and relates to the 'letting to' of anything material. The dye used for the clothes is also very cheap, which in turn relates to the status of the individual wearing it.

The very bright orange worn by prisoners in the American prison system is used so that if a prisoner escapes they can be seen. However, maybe it is also emphasising the fact that these people don't have their freedom.

Adding orange to your environment

Orange in a room can awaken our creative potential. We see this colour in places that wish to attract people and create a social atmosphere. There are a great deal of 'orange' bars around, all with a retro feel but buzzy and lively.

You can create an accent wall in your home using orange. Used around a fireplace in the right tone and shade, orange can make your front room feel warmer and create a social space.

I have tones of orange in my office, as I need the energy for creativity and expansion. I do not flood my office with this colour as it could create frivolous feelings and make me become lazy, so I add indigo to give me structure.

I would suggest that you start with a little burst of orange by including a vase or a bowl containing orange fruit. Your eye will be drawn to the orange, and then you can fill more of the room with this colour by adding cushions and throws.

Playrooms that have orange in them allow for stimulation of younger children and can create an atmosphere of warmth and ease.

Orange stimulates digestion, so kitchens and dining rooms can handle this colour. Be a little careful though, as it may overstimulate and create an atmosphere where food becomes the overriding factor. Make sure you balance it with greens to relax individuals.

Orange for business

Orange denotes adventure and risk-taking, so businesses using the colour orange may be implying that this is an aspect of their services.

A good example is easyJet. This travel organisation came under fire for being 'cheap and cheerful' but now makes a significant impact in the market for short-haul flights. Orange is the colour of travel and freedom, so this emphasises the business's ethos.

Anything to do with children in a business will work with the colour orange, as it psychologically creates the feeling of fun and frivolity.

Orange is a colour that is used a lot in the food industry. A great deal of products contain orange as a food colour (E100 numbers) as it increases our desire for the product. Examples include cheeses, crisps, snacks and cereals.

As a colour, orange must be used carefully in branding by using more subtle tones or combining it with the use of a complementary or accented colour. If you do not get the balance right it can come across as insincere and superficial, and definitely as cheap. In the UK orange is quite a difficult colour to use in business as we tend to be more attracted to the blues, which give rise to feelings of structure and discipline.

Orange personalities

Orange relates to the number 2 and people with an orange personality have the following traits:

Warm and friendly with an easy-going sense of humour ● Love to be with people ● Deeply emotional inside, and fun on the outside ● Creative ● Do not like to be tied down ● Great at mediating ● Can become lazy and just 'opt out'

Orange celebrities: Len Goodman, Darcey Bussell, Greg Wallace.

Orange

Balance colours for orange

The freedom and expressive side of orange can be balanced by the more structured and detached energy of blue or indigo.

It is great to be highly creative with lots going on but to turn your talents into a potential money making venture or to structure a business requires the complementary colour. Indigo is the strongest of these and will bring structure and discipline so that you can build a business. Alternatively, you can add green (or even green and blue) when you want to make money.

Yellow

Yellow is another warm colour that creates reactions of intense like or dislike. I have met people who will not even have yellow flowers in their garden and dislike the colour with a passion.

History of yellow

The name 'yellow' comes from the old English word *gelolu*, which means 'yellowish'. Yellow in the form of yellow ochre pigment, which is made from clay, was first used in cave art.

In Ancient Egypt yellow was associated with gold and considered imperishable, eternal and indestructible. Both the skin and the bone of Egyptian gods were made from golden yellow. Women always had golden faces, which were painted using yellow ochre.

Yellow became firmly established as the colour of Judas Iscariot, the man who betrayed Jesus, and throughout the dark ages and the Christian period was related to envy and duplicity.

Originally, a combination of arsenic, cow urine and other substances was used as a very toxic and cheap dye. In the 18th century synthetic pigments were created to replace these dyes and paints. Turner and Van Gogh used a great deal of yellow in their paintings to show light and to create mood.

In the 20th century yellow was used as a highly visible colour. Jews in Nazi occupied Europe were required to wear yellow badges so they could be identified.

When colour printing on presses surfaced in the late 1800s, yellow become one of the four print colours (known as 'Process Yellow'). It is used to create the array of colours that can be achieved in printing as yellow absorbs most blue light.

Yellow is the most visible colour, and it is particularly attractive to birds and insects. There are more yellow flowers than any other colour in nature, and bees have an exceptionally sensitive eye for this colour, allowing them to pollenate the flowers.

Yellow food colouring is available as tartrazine, a synthetic yellow dye known as E102. It is widely used in foods such as breakfast cereals, popcorn and sports and energy drinks, and is also used in other products such as soap and shampoo,

As bananas ripen they change from the green to become a yellow colour, which is the colour they are when they are picked. The hormonal changes that take place during the ripening process convert amino acids and stimulate the production of several enzymes. These enzymes change the colour and texture of the banana, and the yellow carotenoid produced make the fruit yellow and, eventually, brown when it is overripe.

A room painted yellow feels warmer than a room painted white, and a lamp that gives out yellow light seems more natural than a lamp producing white light.

Yellow is also associated with knowledge and wisdom. In English and many other languages 'brilliant' and 'bright' mean 'intelligent'. In Islam, the yellow colour of gold symbolises wisdom. In medieval European symbolism, yellow symbolised reason.

In many European universities, yellow gowns and caps are worn by members of the science faculties, as yellow is the colour of reason and research.

Physical and emotional aspects of yellow

Yellow deals with the intellect and the mind, so from a physical point of view it activates a part of the brain that deals with mental activity and learning.

It is the colour of the solar plexus chakra (relating to self-confidence) that is situated at stomach level. It works exceptionally well for clearing our gall bladder, liver and our overall digestive system. A nutritionist will advise you to drink a glass of warm water containing lemon in the morning to help clear any toxins from your system, and yellow works the same way.

Yellow helps with nerves and anxiety, relieving the inflammation in the stomach area. On an emotional level it is great for concentration, discrimination and judgement, elucidating warmth, laughter, playfulness and delight.

If you are looking to learn and disseminate information then yellow is fabulous to support these requirements, bringing clear and distinctive decisions into light with clarity. Students can use yellow as a positive addition to their colour palette, as it helps to activate the memory and allows the dissemination of information. Many libraries are painted yellow for this reason.

Yellow is also related to organisational ability and making sure things are in order. Sometimes an overuse of this colour can create control issues and the ability for spontaneity is lost – watch out for this reaction.

Yellow is the colour of the child. Creativity is heightened with this colour but it may be more of a intellectual process than that of orange.

Yellow as a healing colour

Yellow is associated with vitamin D, as in the natural vitamin derived from the action of sunlight on our bodies.

It can help heal the following conditions:

- Nervous system – stimulates the nervous system.
- Stomach, intestines and digestive tract – energises.
- Lymph glands – increases functional activity.
- Spleen – increases function.
- Digestion – assists absorption and assimilation of food.
- Brain – stimulates activity.
- Thymus gland – increases action.
- Constipation – a gentle laxative.
- Bones – rebuilds bones.
- Expectorant – loosens mucus in the lungs and windpipe.
- Indigestion and acid reflux – breaks down acidity.

Wow, how powerful is yellow and its tones and shades.

The more you use the lemon colour the more it is associated with good 'gut' health. Evidence is being reported today that our overall health is greatly determined by how good our gut health is. The more alkaline we become, the more the risk of diabetes, cancer and other serious diseases can be kept at bay.

Yellow mandalas

I tend to find that there are quite a few people who have an aversion to the colour yellow and this seems to be linked with disappointment and bitterness. To help introduce yellow I have some mandalas (pictures) that I use for colouring as a tool. Colouring books have become very popular among adults, and are even available in some of the major UK supermarkets.

You can either purchase a colouring book, choose one of the mandalas on our website (colourministry.co.uk) or use the mandalas at the end of this book. Choose a selection of colours but include yellow as the main colour.

Colour in your mandala and then put it in a visible place – the fridge door is totally acceptable. The colours will be in your eye line and subliminally yellow will be introduced into your environment.

While colouring you will be relaxing and destressing but concentrating on the images that you colouring. Two healing modalities in one!

Yellow crystals and meditation

You can introduce yellow by dotting around your house small crystals of the colour yellow – lemon quartz, yellow fluorite, yellow citrine, mookaite, honey calcite, yellow chalcedony, yellow howlite and many more.

You can also use the crystals one by one. I would suggest using honey calcite or lemon quartz when you are starting out with this treatment as these crystals have a lighter energy and colour.

1. Put some gentle music on in the background.
2. Sit with two stones, one in each hand.
3. Close your eyes and take in one deep breath.
4. Visualise the crystals in your hand – the colour and even the taste – lemon, sharp, clear, soft – and feel the increased saliva in your mouth.
5. Digest the colour by seeing it in your mind's eye, and then moving down your body into your stomach area, across your liver and gall bladder.
6. Let the colour rest there and, still holding the stones, move your hands and place them at this location,

7. Breathe deeply and relax for 15 minutes.
8. Gently arouse yourself by opening your eyes.
9. Stamp your feet on the floor and get up slowly.

You have now let the energy of the colour and the crystals through your solar plexus and into the stomach area.

Repeat as often as you like to help bring clarity and clear your digestive system.

When not to use yellow in healing

If you are already taking medication for digestive problems the addition of yellow may be too overpowering, so do check with your doctor.

Yellow should not be added when people have mental problems and are receiving treatment as it may cause an imbalance and create emotional trauma. Yellow tends to bring things to light.

What happens when you wear yellow

Sunny shades of yellow are the perfect thing to cheer you up on a dull day, so if you're feeling down wearing yellow could help perk you back up.

Yellow is also associated with intelligence and inspiration, so wearing something yellow on the day of your big final exam might help you to apply your positive mental abilities.

Yellow is a summer colour and is much more popular in the summer months, when yellow trousers and tops can be found are marketed by many leading brands Why not add a yellow item of clothing as an accent piece during the autumn or winter?

Wearing yellow can be daunting and the correct shade needs to be selected to fit in with your skin colour, otherwise it can make you feel totally 'washed out'. Research states that wearing yellow can sometimes be over-energising for your colleagues, and it is thought to sometimes make the wearer appear weak.

For the guys, if you are in sales then a yellow tie, not too bright, can be seen as fun and playful. It also creates optimism and a positive outlook on life, so it is great for wearing when with your colleagues or when you require 'buy-in' from your team. Don't wear a yellow tie in India though, as it can signal that someone is a merchant – unless of course you are one!

Adding yellow to your environment

Taking the suggestion given earlier in the healing section, you can introduce yellow by placing yellow crystals or accessories around your home.

I use this colour in darker spots within my home, bringing light and energy to those particular areas. I have a yellow glass vase in the hallway and also yellow glasses in the kitchen.

For my study, I also incorporate yellow by adding paintings on the walls or yellow folders and stationery items to help me organise my working day.

Yellow can also work in bathrooms as it is not as cold as blue, but using the two colours together can create a zesty and lively living space which brightens you up in the mornings.

You need to pick this colour carefully as you have to be comfortable with the shade and tone of yellow that suits you. If you overindulge in this colour it can send you slightly mad and create feelings of anxiety and fretfulness.

'Yellow houses' in Russia are known as mental asylums due to how yellow can make you feel when it is overused. This colour deals with control, and too much yellow can create a very negative mental state.

I also use yellow as an accent colour and make it very gentle. Yellow in kids' playrooms also works well by allowing for stimulus and positive mental adjustment.

Many kitchens are yellow as it aids digestion and is cheery and positive. Again, accent use of the colour helps to keep the energy in the room balanced.

Yellow for business

Yellow in branding is becoming more popular with organisations worldwide, including Nikon, Timberland, Western Union, Ernst & Young and Yellow Pages. Quite a few engineering companies use yellow in their logos, especially those selling or designing precision and intricate machine tools.

Yellow denotes learning and communication of ideas, mainly those coming from an academic and analytical standpoint. It also denotes companies dealing with wisdom and logic, so there are many learning establishments that use yellow in their branding.

Unfortunately, when yellow is printed on white paper it can become a little lost depending on the shade and tone used. It can also cause agitation and anxiety in older people if overused.

Selling leisure goods and children's products may require yellow to be combined with another colour such as red or orange. It is bright and catches your gaze. It is also good to use if you wish to sell off old stock and you are not worried about the price, but don't use it for high-priced items.

Fast food restaurants use yellow along with other colours (mainly red, but Subway uses green) to aid digestion. Obviously, yellow, or the 'golden arches', works terrifically well for MacDonald's, and combined with the red you get faster digestion.

Yellow personalities

Yellow relates to the number 3 and people with a yellow personality have the following traits:

Social warm and friendly ● Childlike and fun ● Likes reading, gadgets, technology and games ● Likes to be with interesting people ● Good at spending money ● Logical and structured when balanced ● Can rush decisions with regrets ● Doesn't like relinquishing control

There are both positive and negative traits to your personality colour. The art to keeping yourself happy is to balance these traits.

Yellow celebrities: Cheryl Fernandez-Versini, Professor Brian Cox, Lord Sugar.

Balance colours for yellow

When yellow is out of balance a person can be extremely controlling and plan every detail. Yellows can also suffer from anxiety and angst, so having blue or green around can help relax the physical body.

To help balance the mind with colour you can add purple, which gives more depth and coolness to certain situations, and add some orange, which will help you 'let go' of any feelings or emotions that are not needed.

Green

Green is the colour of balance, harmony and money. It is a neutral colour and is between yellow and blue. It is the colour of nature and is the easiest colour on the eye.

History of green

We do not find the colour green in the early cave paintings but in Northern Europe there was a dye created from the leaves of the birch tree that used for clothing. It may have been used to hide people in nature.

In Ancient Egypt green was a colour of rebirth and regeneration. They used malachite in their paintings and would dye their clothes in saffron for yellow and then soak them in a blue dye from the woad plant. They also wore green around their eyes to protect them from evil, and often created green amulets in the shape of the scarab beetles for protection.

Blue and green were considered the same colour by the early Greeks, and green was not used a great deal apart from to represent the sea. Romans made green the colour of Venus and created a pigment so that they could use it in glass and mosaics.

Celtic traditions honoured the 'green' man, as he was a nature spirit who would bring fertility to the land. His face can be seen in many churches around the UK and overseas, where he is typically surrounded by vegetation or has vegetation coming out of his mouth. Many local pubs were named The Green Man after such a character.

Green was used in the Middle Ages for bankers, merchants and gentry. Green dyes were made out of fern, plantain and buckthorn berries, nettles and leeks. The dye colour did not last long and also contained high levels of arsenic, making it poisonous. It was not until the 18th century that synthetic dyes were created to replace these natural dyes.

In the 20th century, green was used as a symbol for political organisations associated with the environmental movement, such as Greenpeace and the green parties in

Germany and the UK. It is the colour of hope and new beginnings, and hence the word 'green' is often used to mean young and inexperienced.

The Irish consider green to be lucky but many other nations consider it unlucky. You will not find very many green cars for this reason.

In China green is seen as a colour of infidelity, and it is said that if a man wears a green hat he has been cheating on his wife.

Green signs are used for showing the way. For example, exit and fire exit signs are usually green because if they were in red they would not be seen in a fire (the complementary colour of red is green).

Green is also associated with money and abundance. As the paper for money is traditionally made from trees, many bank notes were originally green.

Physical and emotional aspects of green

When we see anything green we tend to subconsciously take a bigger breath and expand our lungs. Plants ingest carbon dioxide and 'give out' oxygen, which we need to survive.

Green decreases our heart rate and brings down our blood pressure (the opposite of red). It is known as the healing colour and, as it is neutral, it tends to create feelings of balance and harmony.

It is the colour that is the hardest to see for most colour-blind individuals as this condition affects the particular cones in the eye that deal with green. It is also to do with the cones why we all tend to see greens with very different hues and tones.

Green is also linked to the heart chakra and relates to self-love. This chakra can also be pink but I have come to understand that green is the true colour of love. I include green in nearly all of my healing treatments, especially at the end of a session to bring balance and harmony. It can also help us to detach from the needs of other people and creates feelings of unconditional love for ourselves.

Rebirth and renewal are represented by green and it is excellent for helping us to relax and allow our bodies to naturally restore our sense of wellbeing.

The colour of the peacemaker, green builds a feeling of community spirit and sharing space with others. It is a great colour for creating a loving home for friends, family and all those who wish to share the space.

Green as a healing colour

Vitamin E is increased when we apply the colour green. This vitamin acts as an antioxidant and allows our bodies to convert the food we eat into energy. Green also supports the healing of the following issues:

- Pituitary gland – stimulates to increase hormone balance
- Infection – destroys rotting materials, disinfects, kills germs.
- Muscle – rebuilds muscle and tissues.
- Relieves pain – joint and bone issues.
- Immunity – improves immune system and strengthens the nervous system.

'Eat your greens they are good for you' really rings true. In the medical world green is a prominent colour in both pharmacies and hospitals.

Green light

Green is the easiest colour on the eye. The cones in our eyes are either red, green or blue, but 45% of them are green. Therefore our eyes need to work less to perceive this colour, making it one of the most relaxing.

Green light has a positive effect on our circadian rhythms. These are the physical, mental and behavioural changes that follow a roughly 24-hour cycle, responding primarily to light and darkness in an organism's environment, in other words our 'body clock'.

Sometimes when I am treating a client who is feeling very stressed and overanxious I use a green light. I use the BIOPTRON Lamp (colourministry.co.uk), which gives off polarised light that is passed through different coloured filters. The polarised light means that the colour is more intense than average light, which may be more scattered. You can fill a room with green by replacing a normal light bulb with a green LED bulb for as little as £2.50. This a great way to bring in green light.

Green

I would suggest you spend about 20 minutes with the lamp on and just lie down and relax while listening to soft music. Keep your eyes open but do not look directly at the bulb. Look at the glow around the room and let your mind wander.

Do not do this just before bedtime though, as you may find you are unable to sleep. Green can also stir the hormones as well as make you relaxed, and if the bulb is a blue-green colour then this stimulate you rather than calm you.

Breathe and visualise green

This exercise can be done as a couple. One of you relaxes and closes your eyes and other reads the 'green visualisation' below. Downloadable versions of other visualisations are available on our website (colourministry.co.uk).

1. Close your eyes, take one long breath through your nose and exhale through your mouth. Repeat this three times. Feel your body relax and your shoulders drop, hear your heart rate as it slows down, feel the air enter your ribcage and move lower into your stomach.
2. Imagine you are walking through a wood or are out in your favourite piece of countryside. Notice the green trees and the grass all around you. See the new plants growing out of the ground, forming new green stems, the flowers not yet open; hear the gentle sound of the wind meandering its way through the trees, feel the breeze on your face, imagine this wind is the same green as the grass and leaves.
3. As you breathe, feel and see this green enter through your heart and your lungs opening up to take in as much of this fresh, clean, green air as possible. Open up your heart and feel or see the green pouring into it, experience the sensation of love, see the openness of your heart, hear the gentle rhythms of your heartbeat.
4. As you breathe out, let all your insecure thoughts and feelings of jealousy leave your body along with your breath, take in the green deep inside your heart, feel yourself being filled with harmony and balance, let the green surround you.
5. As you breathe in tell yourself 'I am at one with life'. Start slowly to see and feel your breath moving in and out, and then gently open your eyes, take a deep breath and be back in the room.

When not to use green in healing

On the whole this colour can be used in healing as much as required. We are in a flight-or-fight condition on a daily basis when dealing with life's challenges, and we don't have the time just to stop and breathe.

I would suggest that you don't use the green light before bed as you may have already been exposed to a great deal of blue light from your phone, computer, TV or other device during the day, so additional stimulus is not required.

Taking a walk in green can help you to feel more relaxed, and this is fine to do at any time of the day.

What happens when you wear green

All shades of green are calming and soothing and are among spring's most popular shades of colour. All those people who look at you when you are wearing green will get an instant hit of 'destressing', so if you are taking an exam or are anxious about a driving test then wear green to help you feel more relaxed.

When a man wears a green tie it projects a feeling of growing skills and knowledge. It is seen as the colour of rebirth and growth, and is a great way of emphasising his team-player abilities. Watch what type of green though, as it can be seen as a 'chancer' colour if it is too yellow.

If you work for an environmental company or are going to an interview for a job with this type of organisation it would be good to wear green as it is an indication of your personal association with the company's ethics and values.

When you wear darker green accent colours there is a feeling of stability and seriousness about your personality. If you would like to come across as practical, reliable and down to earth, then choose a mid-range green. If you would like to be seen as fresh, energetic and balanced, then choose a lighter green, which looks younger and more adaptable to change.

Do watch out though, as green was used in the Middle Ages for wedding dresses and represented fertility. Wearing green can help you when you are pregnant or even support you when you are trying to conceive.

Green can also give a feeling of naivety and is not seen as sexy, unlike its complementary colour red. Many images show goddesses dressed in green, connecting them with nature and the natural world.

I see the colour as neither masculine nor feminine, rather as a colour of balance, but if I want to increase my bank balance and bring in abundance I will add green to wardrobe and buy a green purse.

Adding green to your environment

Green is the most popular colour when looking at interior design. 'Bringing the outside in' is a common phrase used when accenting a room with green. Naturally, conservatories, orangeries and semi-outside living space are commonly green to blend in with the garden.

I have found that for children who suffer with asthma green is a great colour for their bedroom, a light pastel green should suffice but sometimes an accent wall can help to increase the energy of the colour.

You can add green into any room by bringing in plants or accessories such as vases, candleholders and lamp stands.

Green is great in a hallway, as it tends to activate relaxation as soon as you or your visitors enter the house. Make sure it is not a blue-green, as this may appear a little cold unless the hallway has a great deal of light.

Green is also fabulous in a bathroom, as it purifies and dispels decay and kills germs. Green is used a great deal in French-style accommodation, so you will see green kitchens and bedrooms, which create a feeling of luxury and elegance.

Green for business

As soon as we see the colour green in branding we tend to think 'organic' or 'green'. Companies such as Waitrose, Marks & Spencer, BP, Animal Planet and even Holiday Inn (maybe implying relaxation) use green in their branding.

Nearly all organisations that deal in natural products – from medicines to food and from skincare to drinks – have green in their branding. Pharmacies such as Lloyd's, Community Health and Live Oak have logos and branding in green, and in many countries green is used for signs for doctors and medical centres.

Harrods has green branding that incorporates its name in gold, which is alluring to the type of clientele it wishes to attract, including the privileged and wealthy.

Green as a branding colour can give the feeling of a practical and down to earth organisation with a high moral sense and loyalty to its customers.

Many community groups and social clubs use green as their branding colour, attracting people who wish to belong to a group or organisation. This colour also attracts individuals who wish to be in the 'heart' of their community.

Green personalities

Green relates to the number 4 and people with a green personality have the following traits:

Stable, balanced and harmonious ● Practical and down to earth ●
High moral standards ● Love having people in their home ● Belong to a
community or group ● Can be possessive and materialistic

When there is an overindulgence of green then the more negative traits can arise. Keeping green in balance will help you move towards a more positive personality.

Green celebrities: Bill Gates, Richard Branson, Marie Curie.

Green

Balance colours for green

When green is out of balance a person can become very fixed and fearful of change. The best colour to use with green personalities is orange, which allows for fluidity and fun.

You can also apply red but be cautious, as this is strong colour that can overpower in an emotional situation.

You can also use gold as an accent to green, Gold is the colour of unconditional love and sees everything from a loftier perspective. When green is being devious, selfish and greedy gold activates the ability to balance emotions.

Blue

According to a YouGov report in 2015, blue is the world's favourite colour – in the survey over 33% of people voted for blue. It could be because blue is the least offensive colour visually, the sky is blue and we are all on a blue planet (there is more ocean than land).

Blue is a natural healing colour, cool and relaxing, gentle and non-offensive, so it is easy to wear and have around the home, and when we see blue sky we feel uplifted.

History of blue

In colour therapy we use two shades of blue, as per Isaac Newton's discovery: blue, which is a 'sky blue' a shade lighter than indigo; and indigo, which is darker and contains violet. Blue is a colour that appears only rarely in the world of plants, flowers, vegetables and food, unlike the warmer colours of reds and yellows, which were used much more often in the past for dyes and pigments.

The Ancient Egyptians used blue for painting pots and façias. Grinding silica, lime, copper and alkaline minerals, and heating them to 900°C created the colour blue. Although this process was extremely effective it was a dangerous job.

In the Middle Ages blue was worn by the poor. They used woad, a dye from the leaves of the plant *Isatis tinctoria*, as it was cheap, but it was of poor quality. The dye was made by soaking woad in human urine (which was better the more alcohol it contained) for at least one day, and then placing the mixture in the sun until it dried blue.

At the beginning of the 12th century stained glass windows were introduced in prestigious cathedrals and cities and these contained the colour blue. The depiction of the Virgin Mary also changed people's thoughts of blue, as she was adorned in this colour, and ultramarine became associated with holiness, humility and virtue.

Blue also became a fashionable colour in the 12th century, being worn by the kings of France and King Arthur, and French nobles created an azure, light blue shield sprinkled with gold on their coats of arms. Blue, therefore, become the colour of royalty.

It also became a fashionable colour for uniforms, both light blue and darker blue, in the 19th and 20th centuries. Many French soldiers were dressed in blue, including Napoleon, who is always depicted wearing a dark blue jacket and sky blue breeches. The rank-and-file soldiers, however, wore red breeches and blue coats, which were very visible on the battlefield, so the colour was changed to grey in the early 1900s.

The Impressionist painters added blue to their palettes by using synthetic blues. Turner and Van Gogh used a selection of blues and greens in their many artworks and also complemented this colour with orange and yellow.

Pablo Picasso had a 'blue' period during the early 1900s, when he created melancholy images. This may relate to the English phrase 'feeling blue'. In German, 'blue' means to be drunk, and to the Chinese 'blue' means ghosts, tragedy and sadness.

Blue also remains the colour of the UK conservative party, which stems back to the 17th century when blue was the uniform colour of merchants and businessmen, hence the term 'blue-collar workers'.

In the Hindu tradition, blue is the colour of Vishnu and relates to water and emotion

Blue is a colour that is also associated with sadness, a tradition that comes from Greek myths claiming that the rain came from Zeus' tears of sorrow. A whole genre of music, 'the blues', was even named in this tradition. Soulful singers and trumpets and pianos wail out the tribulations of life in beautiful harmony.

Physical and emotional aspects of blue

Blue is the first colour in the cooler end of the spectrum and is a fantastic antiseptic. Turquoise blue deals with the thymus area of the body and neutralises acid, whereas a more sky blue deals with the throat area. The throat chakra relates to self-expression, and blue is a great colour to use as an antiseptic to dispel inflammation.

Blue is also the colour of truth and integrity, so sometimes when we are having trouble speaking up blue will help us to say what we feel. At other times it may make us too direct and sharp, so a balance of this colour is required.

We are able to detach from situations when we use blue, and this colour is widely used in prisons and mental institutions to keep aggressive behaviour at bay.

Blue instigates peace and rest – we think of the sea and holidays and sunny days with beautiful blue skies. Maybe it is this that makes blue the world's favourite colour.

Blue as a healing colour

Blue is the natural healing colour and works very successfully on the following issues:

- Relieves and prevents itching.
- Allays irritation.
- Neutralises alkaline.
- Natural tonic.
- Skin builder.
- Calms burns and rashes.
- Dispels and reduces fever.

From a healing perspective there are two sorts of blue: sky blue, which relates to our throat chakra; and turquoise, which relates to the thymus (between the heart and the throat).

In colour therapy we tend to work with the sky blue, although I do use a mix of the two blues to achieve even better results, usually when there are issues that relate to the feminine side of life, such as repressing the expression of emotions. This cooler colour tends to soothe and calm situations or emotions. It is great to have around when dealing with issues that require truth and integrity, as it opens the throat chakra and connects to our communication skills.

Blue aura sprays

If you don't wish to wear blue but need to feel relaxed, calm and detach yourself from daily stresses or emotional situations, you can use a spray to add blue to your aura.

There are many companies that make aura sprays, and most of the sprays contain essential oils and also the energy of crystals.

You can also make your own spray, as follows:

1. Purchase some small bottles with pump spray stoppers – you can use plastic but I tend to use glass as it retains the energy.
2. Choose your favourite essential oil, which for you resonates with the colour blue.
3. Use filtered or bottled water.
4. Add about 10 drops of the essential oil to a cup of water.
5. Add a blue crystal – blue lace agate or turquoise.
6. Cover with blue fabric or a blue scarf.
7. Leave in a well-lit area for a few hours.
8. Add 5 drops of alcohol (vodka or brandy) to preserve.
9. Pour into your small bottles and affix the spray tops.

You can then just spray to the left and right of your throat area, and allow a few moments for the spray to settle. Blue is now in your aura and will access your body via your throat chakra.

You can purchase colour sprays from our website (colourministry.co.uk) either as a set or in individual colours from £3.00 each. The blue spray includes peppermint as the essential oil with polarised blue light and the crystal energy of a selection of blue crystals.

Blue candles

Another way of introducing blue into an area of your home where you would like to relax is to add a blue candle. I suggest you find hand-made candles as the essences and energy they contain will be more potent than those of manufactured petroleum or wax candles.

Blue is a colour that helps with forgiveness and peace, so it is great to light a candle after an argument or heated discussion. You can just burn one candle at a time or you can use a selection of candles. Combining turquoise and blue together you will gain a more powerful experience and deal with the throat and thymus together.

It is said that different candle placements can help with different issues:

- Triangle – Overcomes conflict, enhances creativity and good luck.

- Square – Grounds and stabilises and enhances compassion, unconditional love and non-judgement.
- Circle – Protects, creates unity and deep friendships.
- Cross – Aligns and balances the chakras.
- Diamond – Harmony at home and a great manifestation placement.
- Five-point star – Strengthens and heightens spiritual awareness.
- Six-point star – Balances, heals and reconnects the heart chakra.
- Seven-point star – Aligns chakras, enhances self-protection and creates optimism.

When not to use blue in healing

Blue is a cool colour and, although very popular, too much can actually make you feel 'blue'. It is a detachment colour, so you may find that if there is a great deal of blue around you are unable to take risks and move forward.

I would suggest that you add a 'pop' of warm colour (red, orange or yellow) with the blue, and if you are prone to feeling blue then have warm colours around you from time to time.

What happens when you wear blue

Blue is a colour commonly used for uniforms. Most employees in the NHS wear blue: general nurses wear sky blue uniforms, health visitors wear a more turquoise blue and ward managers wear a slightly darker blue.

As I said earlier, blue is a natural healing colour and denotes antiseptic qualities, so hospitals and doctors surgeries tend to dress their staff in this colour.

When we wear blue we are showing that we are loyal and trustworthy. It is an excellent colour to wear to a job interview as it exudes trust and confidence.

If you are a man looking for promotion then a combination of a light blue shirt and a dark blue tie exudes professionalism and gives an indication of being solid and trustworthy.

Blue

For women, blue is seen as an easy colour to look at, relaxes energy and shows professionalism and ability. A light blue top with navy or darker blue trousers or skirt is an excellent combination.

For all you men out there, blue is the most attractive colour to women as it exudes stability and faithfulness. The blue man is fantastic for a long-term relationship – he is dependable, monogamous and can match his own clothes.

Interestingly, recent research showed that the colour blue is a safe colour to wear on a first date. It was ranked third as a colour worn by women who attracted their partner and was also third on the corresponding male list. When interviewed 38% of women said that they would have been put off their date if they did not like the colour he had worn, and 27% of men said the same thing! So blue is a safe bet when you are first meeting someone.

Turquoise, aqua and light pastel blues are great for blonde and white-haired women with a warmer skin tone, as these blues uplift their colour. Those with brown hair and darker skin can wear kingfisher blue, teal and other stronger blues but should avoid pastel hues as these can be draining. Grey hair and cooler skin tones work best with lilac and periwinkle blues, which give a softer and warmer feeling to the skin. Those with a more muted skin tone and with brown or blonde/brown hair and brown eyes can wear duck egg, teal and soft petrol colours.

Adding blue to your environment

Blue is a fabulous colour to use if you are looking for a calm and relaxed room. A den or a conservatory can look great with blue. Do pick the tone of blue that you like if you are going to paint the whole room, as it can be rather cool.

A common room for blue is the bathroom. Although antiseptic and cooling as a colour, you can accent blue with yellow to bring in warmth. You can create the perfect serene heaven when taking a long and luxurious bath.

Blue is also a great colour for children's bedrooms as it is cool and relaxing. It is especially good if your children have a great deal of red energy and are very active. Blue and yellow is a perfect combination for babies, blue and mint green for toddlers and blue and orange for younger children.

As a spiritual colour blue will make children feel safe and secure but with the addition of accent colours it will not become too depressing. Blue can help with sleep and will also create a sense of wellbeing.

Blue kitchens are very popular but I personally feel that blue is not a natural colour for food and is a no-no in a dining room. Blue occurs rarely in nature – no blue vegetables or meats, only cheese that has mould running through it. Blue is an appetite suppressant, so a blue kitchen is great if you want to lose weight but it is not such a good colour for a dining area.

Blue is often used in offices, as studies have shown that people are more productive in blue rooms. Again don't overdose on the colour, because everyone may feel quite 'blue' and you don't want to create 'blue Mondays' every Monday.

Blue for business

Blue is the most common colour for branding and is the safest colour to use when designing logos and websites. It depicts loyalty, honesty and dependability in a business, and helps to build customer loyalty.

Blue works exceptionally well for the corporate world and is used by accountants, insurance companies, banks and other financial institutions where trust and reliability are important.

Hospitals and the NHS are blue organisations where the colour is used not just for branding but also within the wards and offices to help keep locations antiseptic and relaxed.

Blue is used for websites that market one-to-one, and it is also great for hi-tech organisations and computer technology companies such as Microsoft, IBM and Hewlett Packard, as it deals with feelings of security and trust.

My first role was with IBM when the first word processor came about (showing my age!) – not only did we work for a very blue organisation we also wore blue suits and shirts as part of our everyday uniform.

Turquoise blue tends to be used for training colleges, where communication is important and self-expression is used in learning. Outreach programmes, science or research laboratories, private health clinics and complementary health centres tend to use more of a turquoise colour that leads to compassion, healing and balance.

Blue is not a good colour for the food industry as it is not a natural colour in nature.

Blue personalities

Blue relates to the number 5. The following are a few of the blue personality traits:

Kind and gentle ● Faithful and loyal ● Clear and direct communicator ● Hides their feelings ● Sense of logic and order

Blue personalities are natural healers who can keep their distance but give calm and practical help.

Blue celebrities: David Cameron, Simon Cowell, Hugh Laurie.

Balance colours for blue

When blue is out of balance it can feel very 'blue' and tends to distance itself from everyone and everything. Use orange and red to boost warmth into this colour, and yellow can also add a cheery smile to this cool colour.

Indigo

Indigo or royal blue (but with a little purple) is a darker colour than the others and relates to midnight or the 'witching hour'.

History of indigo

Lapis lazuli, a semi-precious stone, has been mined in Afghanistan for more than 3000 years, and was exported to all parts of the ancient world. In Iran and Mesopotamia it was used to make jewellery and vessels, and in Egypt it was used for the eyebrows on the funeral mask of King Tutankhamen

The cost of importing lapis lazuli by caravan across the desert from Afghanistan to Egypt was extremely high. So, from about 2500 BC the Ancient Egyptians began to produce their own blue pigment known as 'Egyptian blue'. This was made by grinding silica, lime, copper and alkali, and heating the mixture to 800–900°C. Egyptian blue, which is considered to be the first synthetic pigment, was used to paint wood, papyrus and canvas, and to colour a glaze used for faience beads, inlays and pots.

Egyptian blue was particularly used for funeral statuary and figurines, and in tomb paintings. Indigo was considered a beneficial colour that would protect the dead against evil in the afterlife. Blue dye was also used to colour the cloth in which mummies were wrapped.

Dark blue was widely used in the decoration of churches in the Byzantine Empire. In Byzantine art, Christ and the Virgin Mary usually wear dark blue or purple. Blue was used as a background colour, representing the night sky, in the magnificent mosaics that decorated Byzantine churches.

In the Islamic world blue was of secondary importance to green, which is believed to have been the favourite colour of the Prophet Mohammed. At certain times in Moorish Spain and other parts of the Islamic world blue was the colour worn by Christians and Jews, because only Muslims were allowed to wear white and green.

Dark blue and turquoise decorative tiles were widely used to decorate the façades and interiors of mosques and palaces from Spain to central Asia. Lapis lazuli pigment was also used to create the rich blues in Persian miniatures.

In the 9th century the Chinese created blue and white porcelain. They exported a great deal of this to Europe and it became extremely popular with the gentry. No one was able copy the technique until the 18th century, when a missionary brought the secret back from China.

Indigo uniforms and military wear became very popular in the 18th century, and many soldiers wore blue. Later, the police force was kitted out in blue, in both the UK and the USA. The colour was indigo and darker than that worn by soldiers. The legal profession also used indigo in their clothing, implying authority, and still today we perceive indigo as an authoritative colour.

In 1873, Levi Strauss came up with a style of work trouser that was made from a robust fabric dyed with indigo – now known as denim. Synthetic dyes are now used to create the colour of denim, and these are not as costly as the original indigo dye obtained from the plant *Indigofera tinctoria*.

Physical and emotional aspects of indigo

Indigo is cool, deep and intuitive as a colour, and has an impact on the all the five senses: arms, hands, tongue, vision and intestines.

It cools and purifies the system as it governs the pineal gland, which is linked to the nervous system. It helps with chest and lung complaints, rheumatism, arthritis and eczema, and helps to stem the flow of heavy bleeding.

At an emotional level indigo gives insight into everyday matters. It tends to be the colour of the teacher and deals with justice and fairness. It works with the brow chakra and deals with self-responsibility.

Intelligence, intuition and knowledge are governed by indigo, and there is a psychic energy and inner vision even if these are not recognised.

Structure and framework can be applied with the colour of indigo, as fear and judgement can become heightened when the colour is out of balance. In addition, if it is out of balance indigo can create ruthless behaviour along with argumentative and intolerant outbursts.

Indigo as a healing colour

This cool colour is associated with the third eye, which is sometimes known as the brow chakra. It covers the area of the body that deals with the eyes, ears, sinuses and teeth.

Adding indigo to your environment helps with the following:

- Depresses the thyroid gland.
- Sedative.
- Relieves pain.
- Stops bleeding or haemorrhaging.
- Is an astringent.
- Deals with varicose veins.
- Purifies the blood.
- Dispels mental confusion.

Adding indigo to your wardrobe is an excellent way to add it to your life. Do not overdose on this colour though, as it can be rather addictive and can also create feelings of depression and coldness as it tends to be very structured and strong.

Using lapis lazuli

This crystal is very powerful in its indigo energy and connects with the intuition. It comes from Egypt and would have been used by the high priests and priestesses, and it was also used for fortune telling.

In the West our third eye tends to be closed. In other words we do not use our intuition very often to make decisions, as we are not taught this in school or by our parents. We tend to be much more logical and to use our mind, which is more about the colour yellow.

To open up your intuition try the following technique, which uses lapis lazuli:

Indigo

1. Find a quiet location where you can relax for 20 minutes.
2. Put on some relaxing music – not too loud.
3. Make sure you have a piece of lapis lazuli that you can rest on your brow between your eyes.
4. Lie back and close your eyes.
5. Place the crystal on your brow.
6. Relax for 20 minutes.
7. Concentrate on your breathing and allow the energy of the stone to activate the chakra.
8. You may feel some pressure on your brow.
9. Be gentle with yourself and enjoy the experience.

Continue to do this about three times a week over 4 weeks. You can take the crystal with you in your pocket or in your purse.

You will notice how your intuition will develop over the period and you will feel the energy accessing your brow chakra. This will help you to develop your relationships with colleagues, family and partners, as you will intuitively know how to react, and it will enable you to stop overanalysing.

Bathe in indigo

Another way of introducing the colour is to add indigo oil to your bath. This is a great way to add indigo, especially as the colour helps you to sleep – so bathing before bed is a great idea.

There are quite a few ready-made oils on the market, and I would suggest that you purchase one of these, as making an effective oil can be fairly difficult. You can purchase oils from our website (colourministry.co.uk).

Neal's Yard produces soothing bath oils in indigo glass bottles, which will infuse the oils with the colour. Alternatively, you can purchase their 'create your own massage oil' and add a few drops of frankincense essential oil. Add a few drops to your bath.

Zephorium makes fantastic bath oil containing frankincense and patchouli, with lapis lazuli already infused in the patchouli oil. The oil is in an indigo bottle, which helps to protect the vibration of the colour.

When not to use indigo in healing

The depth of indigo means that it can be quite a depressant colour if use excessively. If addictions are a problem then adding indigo will enhance the addiction, not stop it.

Indigo also brings information 'out of the blue', which can be shocking, and if the person is not emotionally stable it may cause some distress.

What happens when you wear indigo

Indigo or Royal Navy is one of the best colours to wear when going to an interview, dealing with the law or giving a talk to a group.

Navy blue is always a safe colour; it gives a feeling of professionalism and security. In the past most police forces in the UK and the USA wore dark navy blue uniforms, now unfortunately they are black.

Barak Obama wears navy blue or very dark grey suits. He wears the blue when meeting diplomats, as the colour is internationally known as a great colour for expressing stability and structure. He also wears indigo ties along with a white or light blue shirt, which again appears extremely professional. Various patterns on a base of indigo can be a good choice, as they make a neck tie more lively yet sufficiently formal, which is perfect for various business occasions.

Navy was a common colour in fashion from the 1910s through to the 1950s and to a lesser degree even in the 1960s (more so the first half of the decade), and it came back in full force during the power suit days of the 1980s. While it has certainly never vanished from store shelves entirely, I would say that the 1980s was the last decade when the colour really enjoyed a long run in the spotlight.

One of the great things about navy blue is how crisp and confident it is. You can wear it alone or with numerous other colours, and it always stands tall and remains an elegant backdrop or centrepiece.

It is also possible to mix navy with patterns as well as alternative colours, and vintage navy is very popular at the present time. Orange, its complementary colour, is great to wear with navy, as are pinks, reds, yellows or even silver or grey, which can look extremely elegant.

Adding indigo to your environment

The dark blue colour can be quite intense, and so you will need to proceed with caution with indigo if you are not going to overwhelm a room.

Indigo is a great colour where you can add other colours to give it balance. For example, a clear, bright yellow-based baby pink will jar with indigo, but put indigo next to a blue-based magenta and the colours will flourish.

It's a great colour if you want to create a dramatic, bold impact – for a bathroom where you want to cocoon yourself away from the world, or when you want to create a luxury feel for the second toilet. It's a great colour for a bar or gentlemen's club, so if you have a room where you want that style and feel then consider using indigo.

If the room is north facing, blue could make the room feel even colder. Also, avoid using indigo in the kitchen or dining room, as it is a depressant colour and thus can supress the appetite. Personally I would experiment with this colour first by adding cushions, rugs and picture frames. You could use it in a big living room on a chimney breast or on an accent wall.

I use indigo in my office when I want to create structure and discipline for getting things done. I make sure I always have the complementary colour of orange to lift my spirits, as the indigo can be overpowering.

Indigo for business

Law, justice and structure can be seen with organisations that are branded with indigo. This colour is reliable and very fair, so it tends to be used by solicitors, lawyers, banks (maybe the investment side more than the retail side) and stockbrokers.

As a colour it also implies that you are dealing face to face with an individual. Indigo looks within and is related to inherent knowledge, so we look to these businesses and the people within them to be able to inform us on a one-to-one basis of what needs to be done and how to make the right decisions moving forward.

Many companies use indigo in their logo with other colours. Ikea, for example, uses a strong navy blue but this is complemented with yellow, giving the feeling of structured and organised (their stores also imply this when you are walking round) but also of fun (their stores have cafes and they offer a range of products that can transform your property).

British Airways uses the dark blue along with red and white to represent itself as the UK's leading aviation organisation. Pepsi also incorporates this colour along with red and white so that it establishes a separate identity from Coca Cola.

FedEx uses blue for the 'Fed' (safe and secure) and orange for the 'Ex' (the colour of travel and movement), illustrating how you can use indigo in branding together with an accent complementary to good effect.

Indigo on its own is too intense for an office but accents of this colour will help with structure and discipline. You may find, however, that there is enough blue in business, as it is the most common colour to wear and really is a business uniform.

I wear navy blue instead of black when I am visiting a business but I always have an accent of complementary colour, even if it is just a bracelet or ring, to balance this lovely but intense colour.

Indigo personalities

Indigo relates to the number 6 and people with an indigo personality have the following traits:

> Offer structure and safety ● Have natural authority ● Intuitive and hidden knowledge ● Natural teachers ● Can be fearful ● Their own worst enemy

Indigos can be very cool and not give much away when they are balanced, but they have great foresight and their psychic abilities can be phenomenal.

Indigo celebrities: Gareth Malone, Kanye West, George W. Bush.

Indigo

Balance colours for indigo

The balance colours for indigo are red and orange, to warm the colour up. Red allows you to move forward and get on with life, and orange helps you to 'let go' of any fear and to take some risks to achieve what you truly deserve.

Purple/violet

Purple is the fastest colour on the visible spectrum and also the coolest. Regal and luxurious, this colour is associated with all things mystical.

History of purple

Violet is one of the oldest colours used by man. Traces of very dark violet (made by grinding mineral manganese and hematite, mixing it with water or animal fat and then brushing it on the cave wall or applying it with the fingers) are found in the prehistoric cave art in Pech Merle, France, which dates back about 25,000 years. Traces of purple being used instead of black charcoal have been found in caves as old as 50,000 years or more.

In Ancient Egypt many people dyed their clothes with mulberry and grape juice in order to wear purple. In Roman times Tyrian purple was the most famous purple dye. This was made from puncturing a certain gland of decomposed snails to obtain a milk-white liquid, which then changed quite radically to a very deep purple. This dye cost a fortune, so the colour was worn only by royalty (the average toga cost over €2,000.00 in today's prices).

Senior Church Ministers and Senior Commanders continued to wear purple, as these were the richest professions until the 1400s. Eventually the colour was replaced by red as a cheaper and less laborious option to create.

Purple has always played an important part in religion, and it is customary in the Catholic Church for senior clergy to wear purple. Mary and the angels were depicted in purple by many of the 15th century painters.

Up until the late 1800s purple was worn only by those who could afford it, but in the late 1800s William Henry Perkins made a synthetic dye from the plant mauvene (which became mauve). Perkins built a factory to produce the dye, and many more people began to dye their clothes this colour. It was the first commercial dye that changed people's attitudes to the colour and the fashion industry.

Painters used this colour in the 19th century to show love and they definitely used it as a feminine colour. For the coronation of Queen Elizabeth II there were three shades of purple on her cloak alone.

The women's suffrage movement made purple, green and white 'their' colours, and these are now known as the colour of the women's liberation movement.

Today the colour purple is worn by the leaders of UK political parties when campaigning, as it shows a balance between red for drive and ambition and blue for communication and kindness.

Grapes, eggplants, pansies and other fruits, vegetables and flowers are purple because they contain natural pigments called anthocyanins. These pigments are found in the leaves, roots, stems, fruits and flowers of all plants. They aid photosynthesis by blocking harmful wavelengths of light that would cause damage. In flowers, the purple anthocyanins help attract insects to pollinate the flowers.

Not all anthocyanins are purple; they vary in colour from red to purple, blue, green or yellow, depending on the pH level.

Physical and emotional aspects of purple

Purple is the colour that works exceptionally well on the head area and is related physically to all things to do with the mind. It is a very sensitive colour and is associated with mental illnesses, personality disorders and diseases that affect the mind. It relates to the crown chakra and self-knowledge.

It is a great sedative colour, and induces sleep and lowers the body temperature.

Emotionally it can affect how we feel about the world, and when in balance it increases our abilities of empathy. It is an inspirational colour and allows us to expand our awareness to more than just our physical presence; it connects us to the divine or life-force energy.

As this colour is extremely sensitive, you should use it sparingly. Sometimes it can create difficulties of not feeling grounded, and enhance contemplation and meditation but not taking action.

It is a great colour to help reveal and treat hidden anger. However, it can create a feeling of escapism and can lead to addictions such as drugs and alcohol, which are forms of escapism.

Purple as a healing colour

As this colour relates to the crown chakra, using purple as a healing colour will support the following areas:

- Stimulates the spleen – improves fatigue, decreased immunity and bloating.
- Stimulates the veins.
- Prevents and removes malaria.
- Induces sleep.
- Analgesic – decreases sensitivity to pain.
- Builds sexual power by lowering sensitivity.
- Soothes mental and emotional stress.

You can add purple to your wardrobe and wear it as an accent colour so that you are grounded, and it is useful to add this colour to an area in your home that you use to relax.

Purple yoga poses

If you have a purple yoga mat, use this to lie on. Alternatively, you can use purple cushions or throws or any type of purple material.

You can increase the amount of purple and its impact on your body by doing the following pose (from B. K. S Iyengar, *Yoga: The Path to Holistic Health*):

The legs-up-the-wall pose
1. Place your mat or cover alongside a wall that is clear of objects.
2. Face the wall and lie on your back.
3. Scoot your bottom as close to the wall as you can (ideally touching the wall).
4. Extend your legs up the wall.
5. Let your heels rest on the wall.
6. Flex your feet as though you are standing on the ceiling.

Purple/violet

7. Put your arms out to your sides in a T-shape.
8. Firm your upper back into the ground.
9. Stay in the pose for 5–10 minutes.
10. Do this a couple of times a week.

This pose, along with the infusion of purple that you will receive from your mat, fully stretches and aids in your spleen's proper function.

Breathing the colour purple

Another technique is to breathe the colour purple. This is exceptionally good if you are learning to meditate as it will help you to concentrate on the breath and does not let the mind drift off and focus on distractions. If you are having problems sleeping this exercise before going to bed, as it is a great way to drift off.

1. Find somewhere comfortable to sit or lie down and relax.
2. Breathe deeply and regularly so that you feel calm.
3. When you breathe in imagine the colour purple coming down through your crown.
4. Allow the colour to move around your body.
5. When you breathe out allow the purple to leave via your feet.
6. Continue to do this until you are relaxed or have fallen asleep.

If you wish to do this breathing exercise during the day and do not want to sleep then add the following:

7. Continue to breathe in the colour purple through your crown.
8. When you breathe out make sure the colour is yellow (the complementary colour).
9. The yellow will automatically help you to feel uplifted and energised.
10. You can even add the taste of lemon if you are unable to feel the colour.

This technique will work with any colour, but with the purple it is a perfect way of introducing meditation into your life – a must if you wish to create a life of wellbeing and balance.

When not to use purple in healing

This colour is highly sensitive, so I would not use it when someone is very depressed or at the height of their addictive tendencies. I would also not apply the colour when someone is displaying signs of selfishness, arrogance or being overbearing, as this will enhance these unwanted tendencies.

Purple rules the ego and can completely disconnect someone from the spiritual traits of this colour. When balanced it can reconnect individuals so that they take on a more giving and caring aspect to their personalities.

What happens when you wear purple

This colour reflects feelings of fantasy and magic. It is an individualist, non-conformist colour often favoured by creative people and the less practical side of life.

This is not an interview colour or one that will project professionalism, for that stick to the blues.

It can denote luxury and high quality but if it is the wrong kind of purple or violet then the opposite can also be true. If you want to fit in with the crowd then this should not be your colour of choice, as it makes you stand out from the others.

Wearing a purple tie states that a man is comfortable in his own skin and confident in what he is saying. As purple is a spiritual connection colour it also implies that he is someone with whom you want to build a relationship.

It is also the colour of royalty and wealth, and is acceptable in the workplace. Lighter purple shirts and dark purple ties are very effective if you want to stand out from the crowd.

Many politicians like to wear purple ties when campaigning so that they can build up a relationship with you directly.

Purple is a strong colour and can look overpowering on its own. Combine it with gold, which will make it look classy, even in eye makeup you can wear the purple shadow and use gold as your highlighter.

How about wearing purple with black in the winter? It makes the black more fun and less heavy, and is great for those who have not worn purple before.

Purple and red is a great combination and brings out the best in the purple. Make sure though you neutralise the colours with nude shoes and accessories, otherwise there may be too much colour

Spruce up your grey wardrobe by adding purple in the colder months, and then add a yellow bag or belt just to 'pop' the colours.

Adding purple to your environment

Purple is a fantastic colour for the bedroom, even if it is just used as an accent colour on one wall or in a throw and pillows. Its ability to lull you into sleep as it works on the crown chakra is fabulous but do be prepared that you may also have some spectacular dreams, as it can create inspiration and fantasy.

It can, however, look gaudy if the correct tone or shade is not used, and it can also make a room look undesirably dark. Many teenagers like purple rooms – but then they do spend most of their time sleeping.

Purple combines nicely with other colours both in interior design and in the clothes that you wear. You can mix purple with pale blue, pale indigo and pale pink, or combine it with red, orange and soft yellow to bring warmth and fun into the room.

Purple is an excellent colour to liven up a bland looking room while retaining a feeling of relaxation and comfort. Greys respond well to purple, and this combination creates a meditative space where inspiration and reconnection energies are generated by the colours.

Another way of incorporating purple into your environment is to include it in your garden so that it can be seen through the windows and then using some of the plants within the home. Lavender, verbena, clematis and bellflower are excellent plants for borders and pots.

You can also add irises in the home to add that touch of purple to any living room. Along with a nice chunk of amethyst this colour's energy will help create a wonderful atmosphere, bringing spiritual energies and connection for the whole family.

Purple for business

Purple is used by Cadbury on its chocolate packaging and is also by skincare manufacturers for their product ranges. It indicates luxury and wealth – it is definitely the colour of royalty.

The jewellers Hallmark and Asprey and the search engine Yahoo use this colour in their logos, which give off a feeling of a contemporary type of organisation that has a unique product.

The colour is becoming more acceptable in branding, and TV stations such as E4 and the new Purple Bricks property company have used it to create a feeling of innovation and trend.

It is most probably one of the hardest colours to replicate in the digital world as it uses a mix of red and blue. Computer screens rarely give the colour purple that is true to its actual print colours (printing mixes cyan, magenta, yellow and black to produce the colour).

In Forbes 'most valuable brands of 2014' purple was the least favoured colour but this may be due to the fact that logos containing this colour have really only appeared in the last 5 years.

Many colleges and schools, especially higher education institutions, use purple in their branding. This is unsurprising, as here you would expect to see more individualistic learning.

Purple also works well in the holistic world, with many spiritually motivated people using purple in their readings, shops and branding. As purple is all about connection it is everywhere in the mind, body and spirit world, and sometimes it can be overwhelming.

Purple personalities

Purple relates to the number 7 and purple personalities have the following traits:

Psychically and inspirationally gifted ● Strong spiritual strengths ● Sensitive to energy changes ● Gentle and empathetic ● Charming and charismatic when required ● Can hide away ● Sometimes find human life rather challenging

Purple/violet

Purples make super councillors when their energies are balanced but they can also have escapist tendencies when life becomes too hard.

Purple celebrities: Stephen Hawking, John F. Kennedy, William Shakespeare.

Balance colours for purple

When purples are out of balance they can be very needy and demonstrative, with a feeling that no one is supportive or helping with issues. Balance with yellow, which is the complementary colour bringing creativity and child energies, or add green to bring them back into their hearts and help them to understand that they are truly loved.

Magenta

Magenta is not on the visible spectrum and is not necessarily considered as a colour. It is moving more towards the ultraviolet, and in colour therapy it is considered as two parts red and one part blue.

The colour occurs extremely commonly in flowers, particularly in the tropics and subtropics. As it is the complementary colour to green, the flowers are more visible to the insects needed for their pollination.

History of magenta

The colour we know as magenta was given its name by Johann Wolfgang von Goethe in the late 1700s. Spanning more than 30 years, his classic colour experiments culminated in the mysterious marvel called *Theory of Colours*, first published in German in 1810.

One experiential phenomenon Goethe described was the 'recurring and unexplainable appearance' of an eighth colour – one which would 'mysteriously appear' just beyond violet or just before red, seemingly creating a colour or light loop (circular) as opposed to a rainbow (linear).

Magenta was first introduced as a colour through a new aniline dye called fuchsine (taken from the flower fuchsia), which was patented in 1859 by the French chemist Francois-Emmanuel Verguin. Its name was changed the same year to magenta, to celebrate a victory of the French and Sardinian army at the Battle of Magenta, near the Italian town of that name, on 4 June 1859.

Shades of magenta began to appear in art soon after it was introduced. Paul Gauguin (1848–1903) used a shade of magenta in 1890 in his portrait of Marie Lagadu, and in some of his South Seas paintings.

Henri Matisse and the members of the Fauvist movement used magenta and other non-traditional colours to surprise viewers and move their emotions.

Physical and emotional aspects of magenta

Magenta is seen as the colour of negotiation and a bringer of mental balance. The colour is made up of two parts red and one part blue.

It is creative and very well organised but can also be extremely strong as it is fearless. It is daring, with a will to fight, and allows the creation of one goal and drives purposefully towards this.

It is also the colour of transformation, a chance to change, clear the decks and bring in new ideas and maybe even people.

When magenta is balanced it creates positive feelings of charisma and confidence, when it is unbalanced it can become resentful and destructive.

Magenta as a healing colour

As magenta does not impact a particular part of the body, I add this colour into most of my treatments when I feel that someone needs to take a more spiritual or emotional look at the issues that are going on around them.

Magenta can help with the following:

- Stimulates the adrenal glands – less so than red.
- Stimulates the heart.
- Acts as a diuretic.
- Emotional equilibrator.
- Builds the aura.

Magenta relates to the eight chakra, which is above the head and at the top of our aura. It is said that it holds the Akashic records (sometimes known as the Hall of Records), which, it is rumoured, store information about our life experiences, our karma and our social memories of the planet. Magenta is the colour of soul-realisation and seeks spiritual enlightenment.

Magenta works with the element of self-transformation, allowing us to journey through our chakras from red to purple, and then transform to another level. It allows loftier vision where things are seen from above as below, and maybe where we recognise Heaven here on earth. Applying this colour to our auras can help strengthen our spiritual connection and also see the bigger picture with regard to our daily life.

I always have Magenta somewhere in my locality whether it is a crystal, cushions, a throw or just some great underwear. It allows me to let go of anger and resentment and know that everything changes.

I use magenta more often than red as it is less 'hot' and, when balanced, creates universal harmony and love. Unfortunately, if there is an overwhelming amount of magenta it can lead to dominance, intolerance, and a person can become bossy and demanding, so use it with care.

What happens when you wear magenta

If you choose to wear the colour magenta you are projecting your 'free-spirit' and your freedom. You may become often quick-witted and fit in comfortably with the social scene.

If you wear magenta you are a caring and nurturing soul who possesses a higher perspective and tuned-in intuition. You are bright and determined about the things that you regard as important.

Magenta wearers make great manipulators and actors. You project a creative and agile mind and are resourceful and artistic. Magenta is very good at protecting the wearer's vulnerability.

Magenta ties for men are becoming more popular, although it takes a strong man to wear one – or an artist, in which case the tie may be a cravat! Softer pink shirts are definitely 'in' but usually are worn with blue ties.

Remember, you can wear colours on the inside as lingerie to help you connect with this particular colour if you feel it is too strong for you.

Magenta in business

Magenta can be a practical colour, bringing balance between compassion, support and kindness and getting things done. In branding it is used by companies that want to be seen as inspirational and innovative. It is not pink and fluffy, and therefore attracts both men and women.

Many coaches and mentors use this colour, as it can be imaginative and compassionate at the same time. It also conveys energy, youthfulness and excitement.

Superdrug uses this colour logo and many products designed for teenagers and young girls are housed in this colour. The Athena Network and Women in Business brand with this colour, and of course it was made popular by T Mobile who registered their brand colour as exclusive.

I suspect we will see more companies using magenta in their branding as we move towards a new unique business market where people are working on compassion and inclusion instead of separation.

Magenta personalities

Magenta relates to the number 8 and people with a magenta personality have the following traits:

Fertile imagination with many creative instincts ● Fabulous organisers ● Free spirited ● Can juggle many projects ● Charismatic and strongly entrepreneurial ● Dominant and bossy ● Can become resentful

Magentas are just oranges grown up!

Magenta celebrities: Richard Dawkins, Tommy Cooper, Joan Collins.

Balance colours for magenta

Green is the complementary colour for magenta and brings magentas back into the heart of the matter, allowing them to stay home and enjoy their family life instead of flitting everywhere.

Gold

Gold is a precious metal and is one of the least reactive chemical elements. It is solid under normal conditions and this is why it is found as nuggets and in veins and in rocks.

It may have been that this colour was originally white but became gold as it was used with such great respect in nearly all of the world's cultures.

The history of gold

Gold's history does not have a starting point. It was present on Earth as part of the supernova nucleosynthesis, when the Earth was created, and sank to the planetary core. Most of the remaining gold was delivered to Earth by asteroid impacts about 4 billion years ago.

Our first understanding of how gold was used comes from the Ancient Egyptians who used gold extensively throughout their time. The death mask of Tutankhamun is solid gold and weighs 11 kg. The Egyptians used over 110 kg of gold during their time, and they were very lucky there was so much gold available in and around the North African region.

The gold naturally connected the Egyptians to the yellowness associated with the Sun, and as they believed that gold had magical and mystical powers it was used to create amazing objects. Dwarfs, who were seen as magical creatures, were the goldsmiths of the Egyptian world and created wonderful items that would be given to the gods in worship.

In the Byzantine age, gold was reflected in paintings that were icons to Christianity. It was a divine gift that reflected light in the paintings, and many churches were adorned with gold tesserae (a type of glass) that was put all over the ceilings to reflect the light of God's eye on his people.

The Renaissance era saw the use of gold to create jewellery, and Queen Elizabeth I handed out cameos to her most promising advocates as thank you gifts. Gold was seen as a power and status object only available to the rich.

Gold

In the 1700s, Augustus the Strong was obsessed by gold, making sure that he had more than anyone in the world. In Persia there were many gold owners who were wealthy beyond what we can imagine today. Augustus searched for an alchemist who could turn anything into gold and make him the richest man in the world. He found a young man who spent 10 years trying to achieve this goal but failed. He did, however, make a sun mask for Augustus (out of copper with a little gold) as his legacy.

In the 19th century Birmingham was the most innovative place on the planet, where many patents were filed for new and inventive ideas. On 25 March 1840, George Elkington, who was obsessed with patents, made gold objects from nothing by covering objects with gold through electroplating. When Prince Albert visited the factory he was fascinated by the process, and it was rumoured that he had a gold-plating system installed in Buckingham Palace.

In the 20th century gold was reintroduced in Vienna's gilded age, when Gustav Klimt painted The Kiss, which is filled with various sources of gold. He combined all the traditions of gold in this picture, hoping to bring gold once again into the forefront.

Physical and emotional aspects of gold

Gold is the colour of success and achievement. It is associated with luxury, prestige, quality and elegance. Gold is linked to the energy of the sun and contains most of the other colours. It is a masculine colour and illuminates everything around it.

When gold is balanced it creates success, abundance, unconditional love, wisdom, passion, charisma and self-worth. When it is unbalanced gold can be self-centred, demanding, lack trust and have a fear of success and wealth.

Gold as a healing colour

I will add gold into my healing sessions by using either a gold spray or gold scarves on the body, for the following reasons:

- If someone needs to see the bigger picture and requires compassion regarding their particular issues.

- Is someone is feeling less than generous and is having trouble forgiving someone else.
- If someone is working on themself and needs deeper knowledge.
- If someone is scared of success or has a fear that is blocking them and preventing them from earning what they deserve.
- If someone wishes to move to a higher spiritual level.

Gold is associated to the stellar gateway chakra, the light portal that connects the soul to the Divine Source, the doorway to other worlds and the ability to have a helicopter view of our human world.

The spiritual lesson of gold is to integrate lessons learned in prior lives and achieve an understanding of unconditional love.

Gold in business

Gold in business is seen as representing prestige, luxury, wealth and opulence. Companies such as Yves Saint Laurent, Coutts Bank (the Queen's bank), MGM Grand, St Regis Hotels, Taj Hotels and many more use gold in their branding.

Gold can also represent happiness and beauty, so a great deal of beauty products incorporate gold in their branding and packaging.

Gold also denotes wisdom and wealth of knowledge, so gold is usually used for an organisation that is looking to win over its competition.

Gold is great on printed white paper or as a background colour but electronic screens struggle to reproduce gold to the same quality.

Gold on black suggests extreme opulence, elegance and wealth, so we see people flaunt black outfits with masses of gold chains signifying wealth, if not taste.

Gold personalities

Gold relates to the number 9 and people with a gold personality have the following personality traits:

Gold

Natural teacher in any role ● Old souls with psychic abilities ● Missionaries and visionaries ● Procrastinators ● Subservient

Golds need to be of service to others and to feel part of society, and tend to have abilities that are very rounded, not choosing one particular area to excel at. They need, however, to push forward, as they tend to procrastinate.

Gold celebrities: Jamie Oliver, Professor Robert Winston, Tom Jones.

Balance colours for gold

When gold is out of balance it can be far too easy going and not make any decisions, or it can be very much the martyr. Balance with red to create movement and decision-making. Use green to get to the heart of the matter and join in with society.

Mandalas

93

Blue

Red

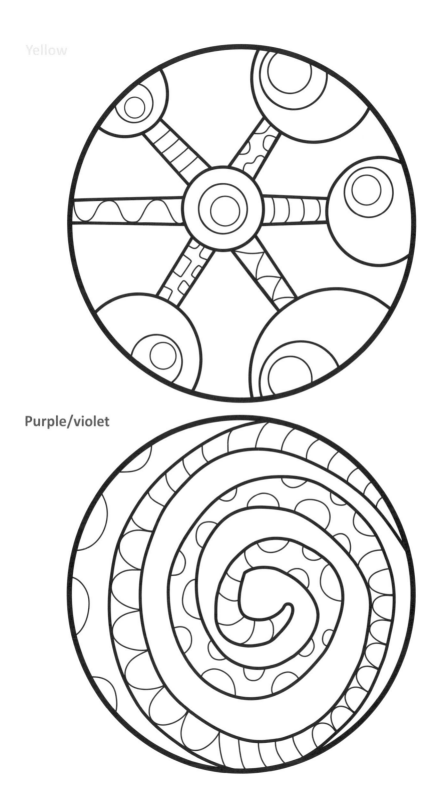

Yellow

Purple/violet

Magenta

Green

Orange

Indigo

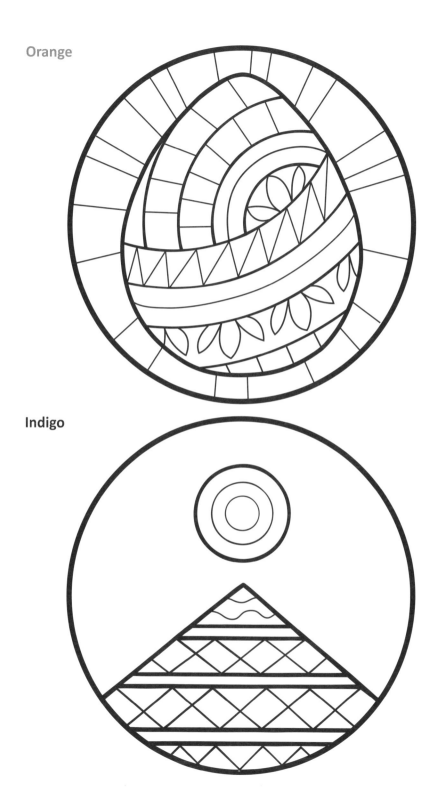

Gold

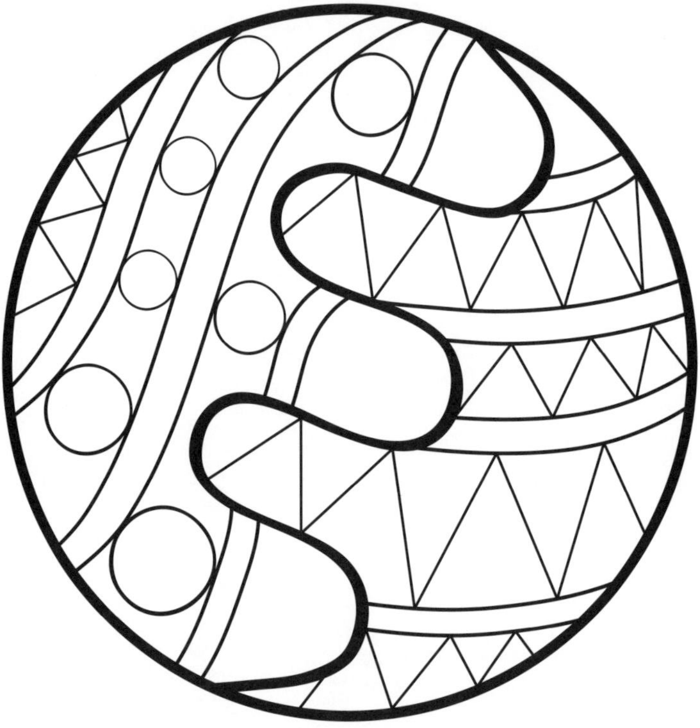

Acknowledgements

Books:
Heal with Colour – Ted Andrews
How Not to Wear Black – Jules Standish
The Art of Colour Therapy – Theresa Sundt
The Book of Colour Healing – Theo Gimbel
The Principles of Light – Edwin D. Babbitt
Light, the Medicine of the Future – Jacob Libberman
Color Therapy – Rueben Amber
The Healing Gods of Ancient Civilisations – Walter Addison Jayne
Colours of the Soul – June McLeod
The Power of Colour and Colour Healing – Sue and Simon Lilly
The Ancient Art of Color Therapy – Linda Clark
Healing and Regeneration through Color – Carrie Heline

Articles – many from the following sites:
www.dailymail.co.uk/sciencetech
www.bbc.co.uk/science
www.collegefashion.net
www.houseofcolour.co.uk
www.sensationalcolor.com
www.wikapedia.com

Data sources:
Dulux research of people's favourite colour – 2013
University of Rochester research on colour preferences – 2014
Pantone services, available from Pantone.com

Pictures:
Fuet, Michal Boubin, Sonya illustrations, chege011 and rasslava

The Colour Ministry

Colour Training

As natural healers, colour and light have many great qualities that can help your body heal naturally and also give you a more positive psychological approach to life.

Our one-day Colour Experience Workshop is great for gaining an overall knowledge of the beneficial effects of colour and light.

Our eight-day Diploma in Holistic Light and Colour Therapy is ideal both for practitioners to complement their existing therapies and for those who simply wish to learn how to use colour to help themselves and their loved ones.

Full Personality Readings

Having a Colour Personality Reading can give you inside information that can help you expand your key relationships, understand your most challenging relationships and make sense of family dynamics.

Practical advice is given on how to use colour in your environment to enhance these relationships.

For more information on The Colour Ministry or to order:
www.thecolourministry.co.uk
email: ask@thecolourministry.co.uk
phone: +44 (0)1903 331234

Colour Parties

At our Colour Ministry Party you can learn how to harness the positive effects of colour while getting together with friends and family in the comfort of your own home. For a small charge per person and lasting approximately two hours, we bring to you the experiences of how colour affects you physically and emotionally.

You will get to know your colour personality, and there is a free gift for everyone, with a special gift for the hostess. With our range of products and our passion for colour this makes for an entertaining evening that is full of fun.

For more information on The Colour Ministry or to order:
www.thecolourministry.co.uk
email: ask@thecolourministry.co.uk
phone: +44 (0)1903 331234

Notes

Notes

Notes

Notes